FOCUS

Pearson Education Limited
Edinburgh Gate, Harlow
Essex, CM20 2JE, England
and Associated Companies throughout the world

www.english.com/focus

First published 2016
Eleventh impression 2021

ISBN 978-1-4479-9817-4

Set in Avenir
Printed and bound by L.E.G.O. S.p.A., Italy

Acknowledgements

The publisher and authors would like to thank the following people for their feedback and comments during the development of the material:
Humberto Santos Duran, Anna Maria Grochowska, Inga Lande, Magdalena Loska, Rosa Maria Maldonado, Juliana Queiroz Pereira, Tomasz Siuta, Renata Tomaka-Pasternak

Text

We are grateful to the following for permission to reproduce copyright material: Article on page 5 adapted from http://www.webuser.co.uk/websites/online-fun-blog/websites/393104/10-amazing-lego-facts, Lego, with permission from LEGO; Article on page 25 adapted from 'Autistic boy's basketball dream becomes a reality', The Telegraph, 12/03/2006 (Wapshott, N), copyright © Telegraph Media Group Limited; Article on page 49 adapted from 'Sam Stern's tips and recipes for student cooks', The Telegraph, 11/09/2013 (Stern, S), copyright © Telegraph Media Group Limited; Article on page 60 adapted from Norwegian town places mirrors on hillsides to shine light into valley, The Telegraph, 23/10/2013 (Alexander, H), copyright © Telegraph Media Group Limited; Quote on page 82 from '50 Rules Children Won't Learn in School' (Sykes, C) 21/08/2007, St. Martin's Press; Quote on page 82 from Cold Hard Truth: On Business, Money & Life Doubleday, Canada (O'Leary, K) p.151, Random House of Canada Limited and Kevin O'Leary, author of Cold Hard Truth on Men, Women & Money (www.kevinoleary.com); Article on page 96 adapted from Tim Robbins back behind bars - as an acting mentor, The Telegraph, 02/09/2013 (Hawksley, R), copyright © Telegraph Media Group Limited.

In some instances we have been unable to trace the owners of copyright material, and we would appreciate any information that would enable us to do so.

Photo Acknowledgements

The publisher would like to thank the following for their kind permission to reproduce their photographs:
(Key: b-bottom; c-centre; l-left; r-right; t-top)

123RF.com: fastfun23 76; **Alamy Images:** BSIP SA 71l, Hemis 35, Juice Images 50, MBI 89, Michael Preston 13l, Kumar Sriskandan 40, David Wall 96bl, ZUMA Press, Inc. 96r; Corbis: In Pictures / Andrew Aitchison 95, Reuters / NTB Scanpix 60tl, 60br; **DK Images:** Steve Gorton 14, Mockford and Bonetti 32/2, Eric Thomas 22t; **Fotolia.com:** abdrahimmahfar 71r, allapen 130bl, alswart 88, auremar 8/3, Goran Bogicevic 20br, Franck Boston 47l, dabldy 56, Philippe Devanne 20tr, Jeanette Dietl 8/6, floral_set 96tl, fovivafoto 20bl, Christos Georghiou 22b, graphit 133, Anton Gvozdikov 37l, high_resolution 132, ikonoklast_hh 15, ioStephy.it 130r, JackF 32tl, kanate 1t, Lsantilli 20cr, macrovector 128, markos86 8/1, Neyak 32/1, nickolae 62, oksix 100, Dirk Peddinghaus 8/2, pixarno 70l, roza 32/3, Gina Sanders 28, Gino Santa Maria 70br, .shock 20cl, silvae 80tr, stokkete 85, THesIMPLIFY 80cr, Dmytro Titov 8/4, valeriy555 47r, vbaleha 13r, Vjom 10br, Tom Wang 8br, yellowj 8/5, 58bl, 58br; **Getty Images:** Archive Photos 84tr, David Buffington 49b, Digital Vision / James Whitaker 37r, Brendan Hoffman 72, Johner Images 49t, Photolibrary / Francois De Heel 37c, Purestock 93, Fox / Kevin Winter 25; **Imagestate Media:** John Foxx Collection 8tl; **Pearson Education Ltd:** Naki Kouyioumtzis 32/4; Rex Features: 13cl, 13cr; **Shutterstock.com:** bikeriderlondon 20tl, 80bl, Bocman1973 2, Greg Epperson 68, Helga Esteb 98, Everett Collection 84tl, Fifian Iromi 26, LesPalenik 84b, MaxFX 36, Monkey Business Images 99, Phase4Studios 8/7, Dan Schreiber 57, Viorel Sima 94, Sylverarts 21, Tsian 92, Dave Turner 32/5, Peter Weber 23; **Survival International:** 61

Illustrations

Illustrated by Jacek Krajewski (Studio Gardengraf) p. 4, 7, 10, 27, 32, 34, 39, 51, 63, 75, 87, 97

All other images © Pearson Education

Every effort has been made to trace the copyright holders and we apologise in advance for any unintentional omissions. We would be pleased to insert the appropriate acknowledgement in any subsequent edition of this publication.

CONTENTS

0.1 Home sweet home

Present tenses – review • Houses

SHOW WHAT YOU KNOW

1 Complete the words in the sentences. The first letter of each word is given.

0 Amy lives **n**_ear_ **t**_he_ **s**_ea_. In summer, we sunbathe in her garden and we can hear the waves.
1 They've moved into a **d**_______ **h**_______ . Because it's not joined to the neighbours' house, it's quiet.
2 Many old people choose to live in **b**_______ because there are no stairs to climb.
3 We only have meals in the **d**_______ **r**_______ on special occasions. Normally, we eat in the kitchen.
4 It's very convenient living in the **c**_______ **c**_______ . My flat is only five minutes from the main station and all the shops.
5 I have a big **b**_______ against the wall in my bedroom and I'm slowly filling it with all the novels I've read.
6 Our boots are down in the **b**______ . Mum won't go there because she says spiders live under the house.

2 Read the email and choose the correct options.

Hi Vicky,
How are you? Guess what! We're moving house again! ☹
I know, I know! It's ridiculous, right? I [1]*hate / am hating* it. We [2]*move / have moved* three times in two years. I'm [3]*just getting / I just got* to know my new school friends and suddenly it's time to leave again. Mum and Dad [4]*are packing up / have packed up* things upstairs right now – I should be helping, but the thought of putting all my stuff in boxes again [5]*makes / has made* me want to cry. It would be so much better if Dad had a normal job. I just want to stay in one place for a few years! I [6]*go / am going* crazy with all this constant change.
Miss you,
C.

3 Complete the sentences with the Present Simple, Present Continuous or Present Perfect form of the verbs in brackets. Use short forms.

0 I_'m driving_ (drive) now. Can I call you back later?
1 Graham __________ (not clean) the bathroom once so far this year. Avoid it if you can!
2 Every September Helen __________ (order) all the stuff she needs for school from that website.
3 What __________ (you/wait) for? The washing-up isn't going to do itself, you know.
4 I __________ (never/live) in a house with a balcony. It's really annoying in the summer when it's hot.
5 __________ (you/really/enjoy) tidying up? If so, you can do my room any time you like!
6 What's that smell? It's coming from the kitchen. __________ (something/burn)?

0.2 National dishes

Quantifiers • Food and drink

SHOW WHAT YOU KNOW

1 Write *C* (countable) or *U* (uncountable) next to the words in the box. Then use them to complete the shopping list.

~~bread~~ [U] butter [ ] chicken [ ]
chocolate [ ] eggs [ ] jam [ ]
olive oil [ ] potatoes [ ] soup [ ]

Shopping
2 loaves of [0]_bread_ (white/brown)
3 cans of [1]_________ (minestrone, chicken, tomato)
a packet of [2]_________
a jar of [3]_________ (raspberry)
a box of [4]_________ (free-range)
2 bars of [5]_________ (milk/white)
a big bag of [6]_________
a bottle of [7]_________
4 pieces of [8]_________ (breast)

2 Cross out one incorrect option in each sentence.

1 Don't put *so much / so many / a lot of* salt on your food. It's not good for you.
2 I would like *any / some / lots of* chilli sauce with my burger, please.
3 They have *a few / many / little* different pizza toppings to choose from. Which do you fancy?
4 I have *few / little / a little* time to help you.
5 *Few / Some / A little* people have actually tasted the world's most expensive coffee.

3 Complete the text with the words in the box. There are two extra words.

a little ~~a lot of~~ any few
little many much some

There are [0]_a lot of_ cooking programmes on television these days. They seem to be on day and night. In fact, [1]______ channels are nothing but cooking. How [2]______ TV chefs do we need? I actually think that very [3]______ people make [4]______ of the dishes they see on these programmes. Perhaps people spend so [5]______ time watching cooking shows that they don't actually have time to cook or eat!

0.3 Flashmob

Present Perfect and Past Simple • Shops

SHOW WHAT YOU KNOW

1 Look at the products in the table and complete the types of shops where you can buy them.

[0]p*et* shop	[1]j_____	[2]s_____ shop	[3]t_____ shop	[4]e_____ shop	[5]s_____ shop	[6]c_____ shop
dog collar	ring	flip flops	doll	GPS	trainers	jeans
fish bowl	bracelet	sandals	game	television	skis	hoodie
cat food	necklace	trainers	Lego	camera	skates	T-shirt

2 Choose the correct options. Then match questions 1–4 with answers a–d.

1 What's the most you have *yet / ever / never* paid for a pair of sunglasses? [b]
2 *Did you look / Have you looked / Are you looking* in the sales yesterday? [ ]
3 Have you decided what you're going to wear *already / yet / just*? [ ]
4 *Did you try / Have you tried / Are you trying* these lovely boots on yet? [ ]

a Yes, I *was / did / have*, but bargains had already gone.
b Well, I have *ever / never / just* paid more than twenty euros because I always lose them or sit on them.
c No, not *yet / already / just*. I think either the black dress or the blue skirt and top.
d Yes, but they *have been / had been / were* too small.

3 Complete the conversation with the Past Simple or Present Perfect form of the verbs in brackets. Use short forms where possible.

A: Good afternoon. Can I help you with anything?
B: Er, yes, actually. Oh! Lilly, it's you! I [0]*haven't seen* (not see) you for ages.
A: Sarah! Hi! Sorry, I didn't recognise you. How are you?
B: Oh, not bad, thanks. And you?
A: Oh, I'm earning a bit of extra money here, you know.
B: That's great! How long [1]_______ (you/work) here?
A: Well, I'm still going to college, so I only work here on Saturdays. I [2]_______ (see) an advert online a few weeks ago. They [3]_______ (need) someone, so I [4]_______ (contact) the boss, we had a chat and he [5]_______ (offer) me the job. I [6]_______ (do) two days since I started, but I already love it! The clothes are really cool and we get to choose the music. And of course, loads of people from school and college come in. Actually, Simon [7]_______ (just/come in). Do you know him? He's so cool! You'll never believe it, but he [8]_______ (ask) for my number.
B: Simon? Simon who?
A: Simon Baxter. Tall, slim, gorgeous! Do you know him?
B: Yes, Lilly, I do. He's my boyfriend.
A: What? But … Oh, Sarah! I'm so sorry.
B: Lilly, it's not your fault … but, you know what? I think I [9]_______ (just/decide) to become single again. Do you fancy going out some time?

0.4 Money, money, money

Comparative and superlative adjectives • *too* and *enough* • Clothes and accessories

SHOW WHAT YOU KNOW

1 Put the words in the box under an appropriate heading.

~~ballet flats~~ belt bikini gloves handbag high heels scarf ski jacket sunhat surf shorts trainers wallet

Winter wear	Beachwear	Footwear	Accessories
		ballet flats	

2 Complete the second sentence so that it has a similar meaning to the first. Use the opposite of the adjectives in bold.

0 Jenna is too **short** to ride on the rollercoaster.
Jenna is *not tall enough* to ride on the rollercoaster.
1 These blue socks are **wetter** than the black ones.
The black socks are _______________ than the blue ones.
2 Tony's arms are **stronger** than Kyle's arms.
Kyle's arms are _______________ than Tony's arms.
3 The food in the hotel was **better** than the rooms.
The rooms in the hotel were _______________ than the food.
4 This ring is not **big** enough to fit on my finger.
This ring is _______________ to fit on my finger.
5 Dean is too **impatient** to enjoy fishing.
Dean is _______________ to enjoy fishing.

3 Complete the article with the correct comparative or superlative form of the adjectives in brackets.

Lego is one of the [0]*simplest* (simple) toys available, but according to many people, it is also one of the [1]_______ (good) in the world. Most adults remember Lego from their childhood. It allows children to be [2]_______ (creative) than with many other toys.

Did you know that there are more than 900 million ways to combine just six Lego bricks? Amazing! Check out some even [3]_______ (amazing) Lego facts:

- The word *Lego* comes from the phrase *leg godt*, which means 'play well' in Danish.
- The Lego figures are [4]_______ (large) population group in the world – more than 4 billion Lego people have been built since 1978.
- In 2006 the yellow used for the Lego people's skin was changed to a(n) [5]_______ (authentic) skin colour.
- Approximately seven Lego sets are sold every second – it's [6]_______ (popular) than many other more modern, high-tech toys.

0.5 At the movies

Future forms • Books and films

SHOW WHAT YOU KNOW

1 Complete the words in the sentences. Some letters are given.

0 Next Friday the school drama group will perform comedy versions of *Cinderella* and other **f**airy **t**ales.
1 There aren't many books to choose from in the airport bookshop. They only have the top ten **b**_______**t s**_______**s** and a few travel guides.
2 It's what all 'Beliebers' have been waiting for – Justin Bieber's exclusive **a**_______**y**. Justin tells his own story.
3 Al would never tell his male friends, but he quite enjoys watching **r**_______**c c**_______**s** with his girlfriend.
4 Zoe loves watching **m**_______**s**, but Dan would rather listen to actors speaking words than singing them.
5 **S**_______**e f**_______**n** films have been popular with many young people ever since *Star Wars* was a huge hit in the 1980s.

2 Choose the correct answer, A, B or C.

1 The phone is ringing. __ it, please?
A Will you answer B Are you going to answer
C Are you answering
2 The students __ their final exam tomorrow at 9 a.m.
A will sit B are going to sit
C are sitting
3 __ some new books online tonight if I have time.
A I'll order B I'm going to order
C I'm ordering
4 I can't come over this evening. Jane and I __ at 7 p.m. to talk about our Science project.
A will meet B are going to meet
C are meeting
5 Look at all this traffic! __ late for the appointment, I'm afraid.
A We'll be B We're going to be
C We're being

3 Complete the conversations with the most appropriate future forms of the words in brackets. Use short forms.

Conversation 1

Assistant: Which colour phone would you like, sir? We have black, white and champagne.
Jake: Hmm, good question. I think I [0]'ll have (have) black.
Assistant: Very good, sir. I [1]_______ (just/check) that we have that particular model here in the shop … Yes, we do. How would you like to pay?
Jake: Erm … I guess I [2]_______ (pay) in cash.

Conversation 2

Molly: Have you decided what you [3]_______ (do) this afternoon?
Scott: Yeah, I [4]_______ (meet) Paul at two and we [5]_______ (play) Frisbee if the weather is good.
Molly: Well, it's clear and blue at the moment, so I don't think it [6]_______ (rain).

0.6 My technology

First and Second Conditionals • Technology and the Internet

SHOW WHAT YOU KNOW

1 Complete the notifications with the correct form of the verbs in the box. There are two extra verbs.

change chat click upload follow ~~log~~ switch type visit

We don't recognise your location. Are you [0]logging on to our website with a new device or connection?

[1]_______ us on Twitter at #Eurolot.

Please make sure you have [2]_______ off your phone.

To open the program, [3]_______ on the blue and white icon.

Please [4]_______ our website to find out more.

To access your account, please [5]_______ in your password.

To [6]_______ your profile picture, select a new photograph, right click and choose 'Make this my profile picture'.

2 Put the words in the correct order to form conditional sentences. Add commas where necessary.

0 the same phone / know / won't / as your sister / you / you / buy
If you buy the same phone as your sister, you won't know which is yours.
1 go crazy / if / would / he / wasn't able to
Liam ______________________ check Twitter at least once every hour.
2 charges / last all day / she / if
Will Lucy's phone battery __________________ it fully?
3 late again / we'll / is / get stuck
If Mum __________________ in the rush hour traffic.
4 she / would / had more time / talk to her friends
If Jasmine ______________________ rather than text with them.

3 Complete the First and Second Conditional sentences with the correct form of the verbs in brackets.

0 If we finish (finish) band practice on time tonight, I 'll meet (meet) you for sushi.
1 If we _______ (not have) school tomorrow, I _______ (go) cross-country skiing with my brother. Unfortunately, it's Wednesday and we do have school.
2 I _______ (not buy) that model of phone if I _______ (be) you. My sister has one and she hates it.
3 OK, OK, you can borrow my bike, but if I _______ (lend) it to you, _______ (you/ride) safely?
4 If everybody _______ (look) the same, we _______ (get) tired of looking at each other.
5 If you _______ (eat) nothing but junk food, you _______ (feel) tired all the time. You should change your diet.

0.7 Growing up

Modal verbs for obligation and permission • Education

SHOW WHAT YOU KNOW

1 Match the headings in the box with the word groups. There are two extra headings.

~~Agriculture~~ Art Business Engineering Geography History Languages Physical Education (PE)

0 *Agriculture* : farming, plants, food
1 ________ : maps, countries, continents
2 ________ : kings and queens, wars and battles
3 ________ : vocabulary, grammar, pronunciation
4 ________ : painting, drawing, sculpture
5 ________ : sales, marketing, accounting

2 Choose the correct options.

1 You *need to / don't have to / mustn't* be male to be an astronaut.
2 You *have to / mustn't / can't* be eighteen to vote in a general election in most countries.
3 PE teachers *mustn't / are allowed to / need to* be physically fit.
4 I*'m allowed to / must / mustn't* remember to send Pauline a birthday card this year.
5 Children *can / must / can't* watch films that have an '18 certificate'.
6 Men *can / must / needn't* wear pink if they want to.

3 Rewrite the sports centre rules. Use modal verbs for permission and obligation. Sometimes more than one answer is possible.

0 Pets are not permitted in the sports centre.
You *can't/aren't allowed to* bring pets into the sports centre.
1 It is necessary to have the correct change for the lockers in the changing rooms.
You ________ have the correct change for the lockers in the changing rooms.
2 It is not necessary to wear a swimming cap in the pool.
You ________ wear a swimming cap in the pool.
3 Parents are permitted to enter the baby pool with their child.
Parents ________ enter the baby pool with their child.
4 It is not permitted to eat in the gym.
You ________ eat in the gym.

0.8 Young entrepreneurs

Defining relative clauses • Work

SHOW WHAT YOU KNOW

1 Complete the words in the sentences. Some letters are given.

0 Ellen wants to be rich, so she is looking for a job that **p***ay***s** a **h***ig***h s***alar***y**.
1 Mum is often home late because her job involves **l**______**g h**______**s**.
2 So, the job is forty hours a week and you will get paid extra if you work **o**______**e**.
3 I don't want a boss telling me what to do all the time. I want to **w**______**k** for **m**______**f**.
4 Uncle Steve has **a**______**d f**______**r** nine different jobs this month, but he hasn't had even one interview.
5 Dad hates travelling to and from work every day. He'd much prefer to **w**______**k** from **h**______**e**.

2 Write sentences with defining relative clauses. Sometimes more than one answer is possible.

0 Sochi / the Russian city / the 2014 Winter Olympics were held
Sochi is the Russian city where the 2014 Winter Olympics were held.
1 an igloo / a traditional type of Inuit house / is made of snow
____
2 a puck / a small flat disk / is used instead of a ball in ice hockey
____
3 an ice dancer / a performer / skates to music
____
4 ski jumping and cross country skiing / the winter sports / Poland is best at
____
5 this amazing speed skating track / the place / three world records were broken yesterday
____

3 Add relative pronouns to the sentences where necessary. Sometimes more than one answer is possible.

0 This is the type of business *Ø* I think people will be keen to invest in.
1 Do you have an idea for a product or service _____ you think people will love?
2 This is the university department _____ Economics, Finance and Banking are taught.
3 Nobody wants a career _____ they find boring or unrewarding.
4 Welcome to the house _____ Steve Jobs lived when he first had the idea for Apple computers.
5 I'm not the sort of person _____ likes to take risks.
6 We are now on the boat _____ Coco Chanel bought after she made her millions as a fashion designer.
7 If you have an idea for a product _____ is more environmentally friendly, please tell us about it.

1 LOOKS

1.1 Vocabulary

Appearance • Personality

SHOW WHAT YOU KNOW

1 Match the words in the box with the photos. There are two extra words.

[blouse boots ~~coat~~ hoodie jacket shirt shoes skirt suit trousers]

0  *coat*

1  ________

2 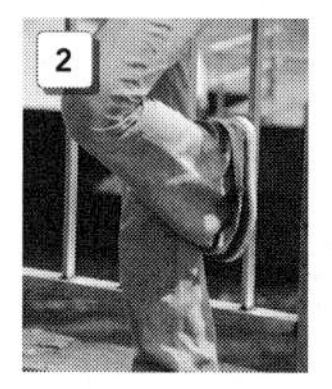 ________

3  ________

4  ________

5  ________

6  ________

7  ________

2 Write the opposites. The first letter of each word is given.

0 tall s*hort*
1 caring s_ _ _ _ _ _ _
2 hard-working l_ _ _
3 outgoing s_ _
4 arrogant m_ _ _ _ _
5 cheerful m_ _ _ _ _ _ _ _ _
6 crazy s_ _ _ _ _ _ _ _
7 curly s_ _ _ _ _ _ _ _
8 blond d_ _ _
9 long s_ _ _ _

WORD STORE 1A

Clothes and accessories

3 Read the definitions and write the words for accessories.

0 A piece of jewellery which you wear on your finger. *ring*
1 These come in pairs like gloves and keep your hands warm. ________
2 A formal piece of clothing which is worn on a shirt and under a jacket. ________
3 These protect your eyes from the sun. ________
4 A casual/sports top which is made of very warm material. ________
5 A single, loose, flexible piece of jewellery which women wear around their wrists. ________
6 This is made of wool and just like a cap keeps your head warm. ________
7 Large rings which are not flexible and which women wear around their wrists. ________
8 You wear this around your neck to keep out the cold. ________

4 Read the report and choose the correct options.

Fashion in focus Red Carpet Report

This week's Red Carpet Report comes from London, where the Prince and Princess attended the premiere of the new James Bond film on Saturday. The royal couple looked extremely smart in their [1]*formal* / *casual* clothes. Prince Nicholas wore a black [2]*suit* / *fleece* with [3]*mittens* / *a waistcoat* under the jacket and a dark purple [4]*bangle* / *tie* around his neck. Princess Abigail wore a gorgeous blue silk [5]*designer dress* / *woollen hat* from her favourite Paris boutique and a diamond [6]*ring* / *bracelet* around her left wrist. She arrived at Leicester Square wearing a lovely old pair of [7]*vintage sunglasses* / *thick tights* which protected her eyes from the hundreds of flashing paparazzi cameras.

REMEMBER BETTER

To help you learn words for clothes and accessories, make a list of some of the things that you own. Include some details about colours, materials, etc. Check any new words you need in a dictionary.

Which of the items in Exercises 1, 3 and 4 do you own? Make a list, then add extra details. Look at the example below for help.

I own a thick, grey winter coat, a pair of black leather boots, two silver rings ...

WORD STORE 1B
Verb phrases – clothes

5 Complete the sentences with the words in the box. There are two extra words.

changed clothes ~~dressed~~ fit
gets matches suits undressed

0 Sophie! Please get *dressed* and eat your breakfast or you'll be late for school.
1 Jack, go and get __________ . The guests will be here soon and you're still in your jeans.
2 I've put on weight and this T-shirt doesn't __________ me anymore.
3 I know it's an expensive bag, but it __________ my new shoes perfectly.
4 Mike felt really embarrassed when the doctor asked him to get __________ .
5 You look beautiful in that dress, Emily. Blue really __________ you.

WORD STORE 1C
Synonyms – appearance and personality

6 Choose the odd one out in each group.

1	mischievous	cheeky	popular
2	adventurous	attractive	gorgeous
3	creative	cute	imaginative
4	charming	adorable	brave
5	elegant	childish	sophisticated
6	immature	cool	stylish

7 Complete the descriptions with words from Exercise 6. The number of letters is given in brackets.

CHANNEL 1

Housemates contestants enter house for new series

Last night the contestants for the latest series of hit TV show _Housemates_ entered their new home for the first time. Here's what we think of them:

Holly – the good-looking one. She's twenty-two and absolutely 0*gorgeous* . (8 letters)

Phillip was very childish when he was interviewed. We think he's the 1__________ one. (8 letters)

Simon – he's so charming! We think viewers are going to find him 2__________ . (8 letters)

Stephanie – a cool young lady. Well-dressed and very 3__________ . (13 letters)

Zak was quite cheeky to his housemates. He's definitely the 4__________ one. (11 letters)

Tina – the brave one. Loves extreme sports; the most 5__________ contestant. (11 letters)

Natalie – very creative; a clothes designer. A very 6__________ person. (11 letters)

8 Complete the sentences with adjectives from Exercise 6. The first letter of each adjective is given.

0 That type of dog is very **c***ute* and makes a good choice for a family pet.
1 My sister is a doctor, but I'm studying to be an architect. She's very practical, but I'm more **c**__________ .
2 Sam travelled all over Africa last year alone. I think he's very **b**__________ .
3 I like British fashion, but I think Italian clothes are more **e**__________ .
4 Your little brother is really irritating. He's very silly and **i**__________ .
5 In Britain TV shows to find new pop singers are now really **p**__________ .
6 In general, children are more **i**__________ than adults and love to tell stories, sing and draw.

SHOW WHAT YOU'VE LEARNT

9 Choose the correct answer, A, B or C.

1 These ___ sunglasses are over twenty years old. I love the old-fashioned look.
A winter B vintage C baseball

2 Your hands will get very cold if you forget your ___ .
A boots B scarf C mittens

3 Brooke wears two silver ___ around her left wrist.
A bangles B mittens C rings

4 You can borrow my shoes if you like. We are the same size, so they should ___ you.
A suit B fit C match

5 Billy, you can't wear your football kit to school. Please get ___ .
A changed B dressed C undressed

6 Kelly got in trouble because she was rude to her Maths teacher. She needs to learn not to be ___ .
A charming B cool C cheeky

7 Luke is ___ . He's seventeen, but he behaves like a twelve-year-old most of the time.
A immature B adorable C cute

8 Helen wears all the latest clothes. She always looks so ___ .
A popular B stylish C childish

9 I admire anyone who is ___ enough to write a novel.
A gorgeous B sophisticated C imaginative

10 India always wears the latest fashions and buys expensive designer clothes. She thinks she's really ___ .
A cool B adorable C brave

/10

1.2 Grammar

Dynamic and state verbs

SHOW WHAT YOU KNOW

1 Read the sentences and write *H* for habits/routines or *N* for things happening now.

0 Journalists are waiting outside the hospital for a first look at the new royal baby. N
1 The doctor doesn't usually arrive until 9 a.m. ☐
2 My cousin is a fashion journalist. She always looks stylish. ☐
3 In today's programme, we're reporting from Paris, the fashion capital of the world. ☐
4 Faraway Travel is currently selling weekend trips to Berlin at bargain prices. ☐
5 We give free cinema tickets to all customers who spend more than £100 on clothes. ☐

2 ★ Read the conversations and choose the correct options.

1 **Jill:** What do you think of these shoes?
Kate: To be honest, I *prefer* / *'m preferring* the ones you tried on first.
2 **Tim:** Are you going to wear that cap?
Danny: *Do you ask* / *Are you asking* if you can borrow it, Tim?
3 **Vicky:** Shall I cook some salmon for lunch?
Max: You know I *don't like* / *'m not liking* fish.
4 **Ellie:** *Do you wear* / *Are you wearing* thermal underwear today?
Jo: No, I only wear it when it's really cold.
5 **Fran:** I *like* / *'m liking* your new suit. Was it expensive?
Jon: Yes. Actually, it was very expensive.
6 **Lewis:** What do you think of the film so far, Grandma?
Grandma: Well, to be honest, I *don't enjoy* / *'m not enjoying* it at all!

What do you think of the film so far, Grandma?

3 ★★ Find and correct the mistakes in five of the sentences. Use short forms.

0 I ~~am not believing~~ Zoe lost my favourite jacket. *don't believe*
1 Is she really needing another new handbag? ______
2 Are these flowers for me? Oh, Jack! I'm not knowing what to say! ______
3 What's happening over there? What are all those people looking at? ______
4 I'm not wanting to wear a suit. I hate formal clothes. ______
5 Laura isn't hating Maths, she just finds it difficult. ______
6 Are you seeing the bracelet with the three diamonds? That's the one I want. ______

4 ★★★ Complete the pairs of sentences with the correct Present Simple or Present Continuous form of the verbs in capitals.

0 THINK
a What *do you think* (you) of my new shirt? Cool, huh?
b You look sad. What *are you thinking* (you) about?

1 HAVE
a I'm sorry, but I can't come and meet you right now. I ______ lunch with Becky.
b Kristy ______ four different pairs of trainers.

2 NOT SEE
a Dave ______ his girlfriend a lot this month because he's revising for his exams.
b I ______ any difference between this woollen hat and the one you bought last week.

3 TASTE
a This coffee ______ really strange.
b Jeremy ______ the curry to see how spicy it is.

SHOW WHAT YOU'VE LEARNT

5 Complete the blog post with the Present Simple or Present Continuous form of the verbs in brackets. Use short forms where possible.

Delphi Designs

Welcome to my fashion blog. I'm Sofia from Athens and I [0] *love* (love) fashion. I [1] ______ (have) my own clothes shop called Delphi Designs on Patras Street. Today is Thursday and that means my business partner [2] ______ (work) in our shop, so I [3] ______ (not need) to go to work. Lucky me! The weather is beautiful, so I [4] ______ (wear) my favourite vintage sunglasses and a simple white cotton top. Personally, I [5] ______ (not like) clothes with big designer logos all over them – my business partner and I [6] ______ (believe) that simple, stylish clothes are always the best choice. Come and visit us at Delphi Designs and see for yourself.

/6

1.3 Listening language practice

Collocations • Adverbs • Relationships

1 Complete the extract from an interview with the correct form of the verbs in the box. There are two extra verbs. Then listen and check.

be continue find ~~get~~ happen last lose stop take

Extract from Students' Book recording CD•1.20 MP3•20

A: It's so easy to make new online friends, isn't it? They ask to be your friend and you accept. It's not as easy to make real life friends, is it?

B: That's right. Making friends online takes a few minutes. But a real friend is somebody you get to know over a long period of time. You meet, you spend time together and you [0]get **to know one another** – [1]**it** _______ **a long time** to become close friends.

A: That's right. But some friendships don't [2]_______ **forever**. And when you don't want to [3]_______ **a friendship,** you can simply de-friend them, can't you?

B: I'm not sure I agree with that, actually. I [4]_______ **it really hard** to de-friend online friends. It seems really mean. I suppose that's why I've got over 300 online friends. In real life, if you fall out with a friend, you [5]_______ **seeing** them. Or sometimes you decide that you no longer have much in common. You no longer like the same things or you've changed. Then you lose touch. You don't have to make the decision – [6]**it just** _______ **naturally**. [...]

REMEMBER BETTER

Try to learn phrases rather than single words. This will help you in exam tasks where you have to fill in gaps. Often the missing word will form a fixed phrase with other words that appear before and after the gap.

Complete the sentences with the correct form of the phrases in bold in Exercise 1.

0 Everybody gets spots sometimes, no matter how often they wash their face. It just happens naturally.

1 All good things must come to an end. Nothing _______________ .

2 A couple should _______________ extremely well before they get engaged.

3 _______________ to qualify as a lawyer or a doctor.

4 Colin _______________ to talk to girls. He gets embarrassed very easily.

5 I'm afraid I can't _______________ with anyone who turns out to be untrustworthy.

6 Zoe and I _______________ each other after she met someone else during the holidays.

REMEMBER THIS

Adverbs of manner tell us how we do an action. We form adverbs by adding *-ly* to adjectives, or *-ily* to adjectives ending in *-y*. (*quick – quickly, cheeky – cheekily).*
Some irregular adverbs (*early, fast, hard, high, late, long* and *low*) have the same form as the adjective. The adverb from good is well.

2 Read REMEMBER THIS. Complete each pair of sentences with the adverb and the adjective form of a word from the box. Then decide which form it is: *adv* or *adj*.

good happy late long

1 Ryan didn't do very well in the race, but at least he tried. *(adv)* / *adj*
Not everyone can be intelligent or attractive, but we can all be _____ . *adv / adj*

2 Will we have to wait _____ for the results of the English test? *adv / adj*
If you want a lift, be nice to me. It is a _____ walk home from here. *adv / adj*

3 I can hardly keep my eyes open. Last night was a _____ night. *adv / adj*
Nina and Eliza arrived _____ and missed the start of the fashion show. *adv / adj*

4 We are _____ to announce that school will be closed this Friday. *adv / adj*
I will _____ wait for you if we can go for ice cream afterwards. *adv / adj*

WORD STORE 1D

Relationships – verb phrases

3 Choose the correct answer, A, B or C.

1 Scott is a reliable friend. He's always there ___ me when I need someone to talk to.
A by B with C for

2 Have you fallen ___ with your sister again, James? Why can't you two just be friends?
A over B out C off

3 Matt and I used to be best friends, but since we left school, we've lost touch ___ each other.
A about B with C to

4 Dean thinks Tim is arrogant. They don't get ___ very well.
A on B over C out

5 Leah and Sophie met on a long bus journey. They discovered they had a lot ___ common.
A of B with C in

6 Dan and John started hanging ___ together after they met at an English club.
A out B with C in

1.4 Reading

Unusual appearances • Compound adjectives

Glossary

transformed (v) = changed completely
costume (n) = clothes that make you look like something, e.g. an animal or a famous person
reflection (n) = an image you can see in a mirror, glass or water
wrinkled (adj) = skin or cloth that is wrinkled has small lines or folds in it

1 Read texts 1–3 and match them with photos A–C.

1 ☐ 2 ☐ 3 ☐

2 Choose the correct answer, A, B, C or D.

1 According to Text 1, Herbert Chavez uses his new appearance
- A to earn money.
- B to educate and entertain.
- C to promote his business.
- D to remind him of his childhood.

2 Text 2 describes a change in Fiona's
- A behaviour.
- B daily routine.
- C appearance.
- D social life.

3 The author of Text 3 wants to
- A announce a competition.
- B offer advice.
- C advertise a company.
- D tell a story.

3 Read the texts again. Are the statements true (T) or false (F)?

1 Herbert Chavez has been a fan of Superman since childhood. ☐
2 Herbert Chavez is unemployed. ☐
3 Fiona works at a school. ☐
4 Fiona slept through her alarm on the morning of the story. ☐
5 Oddfaces is an advertising agency. ☐
6 You don't have to be young to work for Oddfaces. ☐

4 Match the underlined words in the texts with their synonyms.

0 extremely frightened = *terrified*
1 operations = ________
2 ten years = ________
3 strange = ________
4 poorly = ________
5 massive = ________

REMEMBER BETTER

When you learn a new word, look in a dictionary and see if you can also learn a synonym or a phrase with a similar meaning. In this way you will expand your vocabulary. To help you remember the words, write a sentence in which both items fit and add it to your vocabulary notes.

Complete each sentence with a pair of synonyms from Exercise 4.

0 Polly was *extremely frightened/terrified* of thunder and lightning.
1 The first time I saw a *Batman* film was over ________ ago.
2 Since her skiing accident, poor Marta has had three ________ on her leg.
3 Lewis has a(n) ________ tattoo that covers both arms, his chest and the whole of his back.
4 Lola's facial piercing looks very ________ . At first, I thought it was a big spot!
5 Both Claire and Emily think they did very ________ in the Physics exam.

WORD STORE 1E

Compound adjectives – appearance

5 Write the words in the box in the correct groups to make compound adjectives. There are two extra words.

~~-aged~~ well- -eyed -looking -haired -tanned -skinned -handed

0 middle-*aged*
1 short/long/fair/dark/red________
2 right/left________
3 brown/blue/green________
4 light/pale/dark________
5 ________dressed/built

6 Choose the correct options.

1 My cousin prefers *dark / right / middle*-haired men, but she can't explain why.
2 Tom is *well / short / fair*-sighted, so he can see things that are close to him but not things that are far away.
3 In most Asian countries, it's not cool to be *sun / brown / skin*-tanned. Lighter skin is preferred.
4 You don't necessarily have to buy expensive clothes to be well-*built / looking / dressed*.
5 Many women say it's quite common for *long / well / middle*-aged men to stop caring about how they look.
6 In the past people in some countries used to think that *short / left / good* -handed people were evil.
7 At Oddfaces Modelling Agency, you don't need to be *good / red / light*-looking to be successful.

1

NEWS

Thirty-five-year-old Herbert Chavez from the Philippines has transformed himself from an ordinary dress maker into a real-life Superman. After nineteen surgeries that copy the comic book hero's look, Chavez has become a real-life Clark Kent.

Herbert first fell in love with the superhero when he was five years old. Since then he has spent around 300,000 pesos (£4,400) on his obsession – a huge amount of money compared to the average wage in the Philippines.

When he's not making dresses, Herbert can often be seen in the streets around his home, dressed as Superman. He aims to teach children good morals and have some fun at the same time.

Herbert says he feels like a superhero whenever he pulls on the costume, but his mission is not to save the world, but to help in his own small way and bring a smile to the faces of local children.

2

Sleepily, Fiona switched off the alarm clock and tried to wake up fully. It was Monday again and she had another busy week ahead. With only four weeks until her final exams, there was lots of hard work to do and no time for her social life. She really wanted to be older, already finished with school, already earning. Perhaps because winter was coming and it was still cold and dark outside, she found it especially difficult to get out of bed this morning. Her legs felt heavy and she seemed to have less energy than usual. Maybe she had slept badly. Finally, she made it to the bathroom, switched on the light and stood by the sink. When she saw her reflection in the mirror, she screamed. Looking back at her was the face of a terrified old woman – herself, but wrinkled, pale and grey-haired.

3

At Oddfaces we like our models to be fabulously fat or superbly skinny, ten-feet tall or shockingly short. We love odd models with tattoos, piercings and memorable faces.

We have over 1,000 unique character models between the ages of eighteen and ninety-eight and sizes 7 and 27. Our models can bring a truly eye-catching look to music videos, TV shows and films, and of course, print and film advertising. For over a decade, we have successfully provided the most unusual faces and bodies for top fashion designers, photographers and film directors.

If you need beautifully strange and strangely beautiful people, then look no further.

Pretty faces are everywhere these days. Choose something different. Choose Oddfaces.

A

B

C

1.5 Grammar

Present Perfect Continuous

SHOW WHAT YOU KNOW

1 Complete the sentences with the Present Perfect Simple form of the verbs in brackets. Use short forms.

0 Claire *has disliked* (dislike) Danny since they first met at Julia's party.
1 _______ (you/know) Megan for a long time?
2 I _______ (never/understand) why people pay so much for brand name clothing.
3 How long _______ (Chloe/want) to be a fashion designer?
4 _______ (they/see) all the paintings in the gallery yet?
5 Grandma _______ (not need) glasses since she had the eye operation.

2 ★ Complete the tour guide's speech with the Present Perfect Continuous form of the verbs in brackets.

'Welcome to our kilt factory. We hope you enjoy the tour. [0]*Have you been waiting* (you/wait) long? I hope not. Our company [1]_______ (produce) kilts for over 150 years. Today we are going to see how a traditional Scottish kilt is made. We [2]_______ (make) our famous Highlander model since the 1920s. Originally, kilts were designed for everyday use, but later they were worn only on more formal occasions. We [3]_______ (sell) more and more of them as fashion items in recent years. We also make trousers here at the factory, but we [4]_______ (not do) that for as long. Now sir, I see that you are wearing one of our kilts. You look wonderful! [5]_______ (you/buy) our brand for a long time?'

3 ★★ Charlie and Mary are at an art gallery. Choose the correct options to complete their conversation.

M: Can we rest for a minute, Charlie? We [1]*haven't stopped / haven't been stopping* since we got here. I'm exhausted!
C: Sure. We [2]*'ve walked / 've been walking* around since nine. Let's get a coffee.
M: Great. I [3]*haven't had / haven't been having* a drink since this morning.

In the café:

C: There are some lovely paintings here, don't you think?
M: Yeah, lovely. It [4]*'s been / 's been being* a great morning.
C: Listen, Mary, I [5]*'ve waited / 've been waiting* for the right moment to talk to you.
M: Really? What is it?
C: Well, we are good friends and we [6]*'ve liked / 've been liking* each other for a long time, right?
M: Yes, Charlie. [7]*We've spent / 've been spending* more and more time together recently. What do you want to say?
C: Well, do you think you and I could maybe … er …
M: Yes?
C: … study for our exams together?
M: Oh … er … yes, Charlie, I suppose we could.

4 ★★★ Complete the sentences in each pair with the Present Perfect Simple and Present Perfect Continuous form of the verbs in capitals.

0 **READ**
a Rebecca *has been reading* that novel all day.
b Rebecca *has read* five books this year.

1 **LOOK**
a James and Kirsty _______ at photos all morning.
b James and Kirsty _______ at most of the photos from the school trip.

2 **SAVE**
a How long _______ (you) money for a new phone?
b How much money _______ (you) this year?

3 **COLLECT**
a Dan _______ over 200 different *Spiderman* comics.
b Dan _______ comics for seven years.

4 **NOT PLAY**
a Karen _______ football since she broke her leg last year.
b Karen _______ chess for very long, so she still forgets the rules sometimes.

SHOW WHAT YOU'VE LEARNT

5 Complete the text with the Present Perfect Simple or Present Perfect Continuous form of the verbs in the box. There are two extra verbs.

~~buy~~ change contact have help not read watch wear work

Emma Brady Stylists

[0]*Have you bought* (you) any new clothes this year? How long [1]_______ (you) the same old shoes? How many times [2]_______ (you) your hairstyle this year? If you [3]_______ fashion magazines recently because you've been too busy, but want to know what is stylish right now, then maybe I can help. My name is Emma Brady and I'm a personal stylist and shopping consultant. For the last four years, my colleagues and I [4]_______ men and women to choose clothes, shoes and hairstyles that really suit them. Since I started my business, I [5]_______ with over 200 customers. We [6]_______ some very famous people as extremely satisfied clients. Contact us now at em@ebstyle.net.

/6

1.6 Speaking language practice

Talking about a photo

1 Put the adjectives in brackets in the correct order to complete the message.

Hi, Kat – just back from the sales. Got some real bargains! First thing I bought was a [0] *cute* [1]_____ [2]_____ (grey, woollen, cute) hat and a [3]_____ [4]_____ [5]_____ (silver-grey, long, lovely) scarf. They only had [6]_____ [7]_____ (leather, old-fashioned) gloves in the sale, so I'll have to keep looking for those. I also found a coat, finally! It's a [8]_____ [9]_____ [10]_____ (black, mid-length, smart) raincoat and it was reduced by fifty percent! See you at seven – fingers crossed it stays cold and wet – I want to wear my new stuff. ;) Tina x

2 Put the words in the correct order to form phrases.

0 photo, / I / this / see / in / can
In this photo, I can see ...

1 standing / he's / background / the / in
_____

2 stylish / she / think / very / looks / I
_____

3 they / be / at / seem / a / to / fashion show
_____

4 looks / as / changing / they / if / are / a / in / it / room
_____

5 hard / it's / what / to / man / make / the / is / out / wearing
_____

3 Are these phrases used to show uncertainty (U), speculate (S) or give an opinion (O)?

0 probably [S]
1 I don't think ... [ ]
2 I'm not sure, but ... [ ]
3 ... looks as though ... [ ]
4 It's hard to say, but ... [ ]
5 I imagine ... [ ]
6 ... seems to be ... [ ]

4 Complete the description with the phrases in Exercise 3. The first letter of each word is given.

This photo shows a woman and a little boy shopping together. They are [0]**p***robably* mother and son. [1]**I**_____ **h**_____ **t**_____ **s**_____ exactly how old the little boy is, but he [2]**s**_____ **t**_____ **b**_____ about seven or eight. The woman is wearing casual clothes and comfortable shoes and the boy is dressed like a superhero! He looks very unhappy though. In fact, it [3]**l**_____ **a**_____ **t**_____ he is crying. I think they are in a children's clothes shop because the clothes on sale look very small and in the background there are other adults with young children.

The woman is showing the boy a white shirt and a tie – [4]**I i**_____ they are shopping for a school uniform, but [5]**I d**_____ **t**_____ he likes it. [6]**I**_____ **n**_____ **s**_____, **b**_____ maybe the boy is upset because he'd prefer to wear his superhero clothes to school.

5 Find and correct the mistakes in four of the sentences.

0 I think he doesn't look very happy.
I *don't think he looks* very happy.

1 I think she hasn't bought anything.
I _____ bought anything.

2 I think they're very elegant.
I _____ elegant.

3 I think those trousers won't fit her.
I _____ fit her.

4 I think they don't agree on which one to buy.
I _____ agree on which one to buy.

5 I think green doesn't suit him.
I _____ him.

6 I don't think she's attractive.
I _____ attractive.

6 Read the description and choose the correct options.

In this photo I can [1]*show / see* three young women. They are [2]*probably / as though* in a hairdressing salon because the woman on the left [3]*has cut / is cutting* the blond girl's hair. The hairdresser looks quite young and a bit nervous or [4]*perhaps / probably* she is just concentrating on what she is doing. It's [5]*hard / sure* to say, but I think the woman [6]*in / on* the right is checking what the hairdresser is doing. She's dressed quite smartly and [7]*seems / imagines* to be an instructor or the boss, so maybe the hairdresser is still in training. Personally, I would never go to a trainee hairdresser, but I [8]*think the blond girl isn't / don't think the blond girl is* too worried. She's smiling and looks very relaxed. Maybe she's happy because she is getting a free haircut!

1.7 Writing

A description of a person

1 Match the sentence halves.

0 He's in his [g]
1 She's the sort of person who [ ]
2 She's got long [ ]
3 He sometimes [ ]
4 She looks [ ]
5 He usually wears [ ]
6 She's not always [ ]

a like a film star.
b hard-working.
c hangs out with us.
d loves kids.
e fashionable clothes.
f blond hair.
g mid-twenties.

2 Put the words in the correct order to complete the sentences.

0 in / early / thirties / her / is
Becky *is in her early thirties* .
1 who / kind / person / always / your / remembers / the birthday / of / is
Lucas ______________________ .
2 a / make / would / doctor / great
Lucy ______________________ .
3 beautiful / hair / long / blond / got
Marta's ______________________ .
4 bit / is / too / a / slim
Liam ______________________ .
5 kind / unusual / of / looks
Roxanne ______________________ .
6 interested / is / not / fashion / in / really
Peter ______________________ .

3 Complete the conversation with the words in the box. There are two extra words.

built casual dark dresses easy-going friendly height into looks ~~our~~ type

Hi, Jake.

Hi, Adam.

I'm meeting Josh later. U coming out?

Josh?????

U know Josh, don't you? Ed's cousin.

Not sure. What does he look like?

He's [0] *our* age, with long [1] ________ hair.

?

He's got a(n) [2] ________ face.

What?

Oh come on, Adam. He's medium [3] ________ and fairly well- [4] ________ . You know him!

Do I?

He [5] ________ a bit like Ed. He always [6] ________ in black and he's [7] ________ Goth music.

Oh! U mean 'Goth Josh'. Yeah, he's a(n) [8] ________ guy. What time are we meeting?

SHOW WHAT YOU'VE LEARNT

4 Read part of an email you have received from your English friend Harry and write your reply.

It's great to hear that your friend Ben is coming to stay with us in the summer. What does he look like? Is he very friendly like you? Does he like sports and music? I'm sure we're going to have a brilliant time!

Write your email in 140–190 words.

SHOW THAT YOU'VE CHECKED

In my email:

- I have started with a friendly greeting (e.g. *Dear James* or *Hi Gemma*). [ ]
- I have said why I am writing. [ ]
- I have described my friend's appearance (hair, eyes, face, height, build, clothes). [ ]
- I have described my friend's personality and interests. [ ]
- I have thanked the family. [ ]
- I have used contractions (e.g. *I'm, aren't, that's*). [ ]
- I have used some emoticons (☺) and abbreviations (e.g. *info, cu, gr8*) – but not too many! [ ]
- I have finished with a friendly goodbye, (e.g. *Bye 4 now, All the best, Lots of love*). [ ]
- I have checked my spelling and punctuation. [ ]
- I have written at least 140 words. [ ]

1.8 Use of English

Key word transformations

1 For questions 1–6, complete the second sentence so that it has a similar meaning to the first sentence, using the word given. Do not change the word given. You must use between two and five words, including the word given. There is an example.

0 It's strange, but I don't share a lot of interests with my best friend.
COMMON
It's strange, but I don't _have a lot in common_ with my best friend.

1 Josh started wearing suits when he left university.
SINCE
Josh ________ he left university.

2 Paul is always willing to help me when I need him.
THERE
Paul will ________ for me when I need him.

3 It's possible to inherit the gene for baldness from your mother.
CAN
The gene for baldness ________ from your mother.

4 When I met my girlfriend, I became interested in fashion.
BEEN
I ________ interested in fashion until I met my girlfriend.

5 A long time ago, young people wore uncomfortable clothes.
USED
Young people ________ comfortable clothes a long time ago.

6 The photos are different because one was taken outside and the other inside.
IS
The main ________ that one was taken outside and the other inside.

TIPS:

Question 1: Josh started wearing suits in the past and still wears them now!
Question 2: Which expression describes someone who is always willing to help?
Question 3: Think of a way to change the position of the subject in the sentence.

Open cloze

2 For questions 1–10, read the article below and think of the word which best fits each gap. Use only one word in each gap. There is an example at the beginning.

Can we be friends with our parents?

It'd be great if everyone [0]_got_ on better with their parents, wouldn't it? We asked some of our site users to suggest ways of building better relationships with mum and dad.

Carla from Brazil: The most important thing, I think, is to try and share the daily tasks and responsibilities [1]______ of letting your parents do everything for you. Teenagers sometimes [2]______ their parents as bankers, cooks or cleaners, which is going to cause problems in any relationship.

Fred from the USA: You need to think about their feelings as [3]______ as your own. How are my parents going to feel if I seem ashamed of them [4]______ my friends are there? Or if I get mad at them [5]______ time they call me to see how I'm doing?

Ewa from Poland: The most important thing is to be honest. Telling the [6]______ is essential if you want your parents' trust. Everyone wants to lie about their mistakes in [7]______ to avoid getting into trouble. But it only makes things [8]______ if they DO find out. And parents almost [9]______ get to know about what you've done wrong. Everyone makes mistakes, of course, but [10]______ mature means handling your mistakes responsibly and honestly.

TIPS:

Question 1: This word joins two things together: one that we do or want and one that we don't.
Question 2: Which word could you use here to mean the same as 'think of'?
Question 3: Which word completes the phrase meaning 'and also'?

1.9 Self-assessment

1 For each learning objective, tick the box that best matches your ability.

☺☺ = I understand and can help a friend.
☺ = I understand and can do it by myself.
☹ = I understand some, but have some questions.
☹☹ = I do not understand.

			☺☺	☺	☹	☹☹	Need help?
1.1	Vocabulary	I can describe people's appearance and talk about their personality.					Students' book pages 12–13 Word Store page 3 Workbook pages 8–9
1.2	Grammar	I can understand the difference between dynamic and state verbs and use them correctly.					Students' book page 14 Workbook page 10
1.3	Listening	I can understand the main points of a radio programme about friendship.					Students' book page 15 Workbook page 11
1.4	Reading	I can understand the main points of an article about genes.					Students' book pages 16–17 Workbook pages 12–13
1.5	Grammar	I can use the Present Perfect Simple and Continuous.					Students' book page 18 Workbook page 14
1.6	Speaking	I can describe clothes and speculate about people in photos.					Students' book page 19 Workbook page 15
1.7	Writing	I can describe a person in an email.					Students' book pages 20–21 Workbook page 16

2 What can you remember from this unit?

New words I learned (the words you most want to remember from this unit)	**Expressions and phrases I liked** (any expressions or phrases you think sound nice, useful or funny)	**English I heard or read outside class** (e.g. from websites, books, adverts, films, music)

1.10 Self-check

1 Complete the sentences with the words in the box. There are two extra words.

bangles bracelet fleece
mittens ring ~~scarf~~ suit tie

0 Most heat is lost through the head, so wear a hat and a *scarf* round your neck to stay really warm.
1 Stella bought a really cheap _______ and after a few days the finger she wore it on turned green.
2 Wear a thermal top with a _______ over the top and then a jacket. You can put the jacket in your backpack if you get too hot up the mountain.
3 Gavin doesn't know how to tie a _______ . He had to ask his dad to do it for him.
4 I don't like _______ because it's impossible to do anything with your fingers when you are wearing them. I have gloves instead.
5 David, we are going to a funeral! Of course you have to wear a _______ !

/5

2 Choose the correct answer, A, B or C.

0 Everyone seems to like Ollie. Personally, I think he's arrogant and I can't understand why he's so ___ .
A adventurous B lazy (C popular)
1 These kittens are all so cute. How am I supposed to choose just one when they are all so ___ ?
A cheeky B adorable C sophisticated
2 I know it's not very ___ , but I think I'd like money for my birthday if that's OK.
A imaginative B immature C modest
3 I think Sam was very ___ to go backpacking on his own. I would be too scared to go alone.
A gorgeous B brave C childish
4 Yeah, I really like Polly, but I wouldn't want to ___ with her all the time. She talks too much.
A hang out B get on well C lose touch
5 Charlie is ___ . He has always done a lot of sport and recently he started working out at the gym.
A blue-eyed B good-looking C well-built

/5

3 Complete the words in the sentences. The first letter in each word is given.

0 I don't get on very **w***ell* with my brother. We aren't close and we often argue.
1 Are you going to wear your pyjamas all day? Don't you think you should get **d**_______ ?
2 Whenever I've had problems or been upset, my mum has always been **t**_______ for me.
3 Fair-**h**_______ people tend to get sunburnt very quickly.
4 I'm almost ready, Dad. I just need to finish drying my hair and get **c**_______ into my dress.
5 Delilah's parents aren't old. They are in their forties, so I would describe them as middle-**a**_______ .

/5

4 Complete the sentences with the correct form of the verbs in brackets. Sometimes more than one answer is possible.

0 Every time I see you, you *look* (look) completely different. I love your new hairstyle!
1 I _________ (not believe) you, Hannah. You've lied about this so many times.
2 Ian _________ (dance) with Kelly at the moment.
3 Ben _________ (need) to see a doctor about his cough.
4 _________ (you/put) raisins in Dad's birthday cake again this year? Please don't. I hate them!
5 Kim _________ (not know) how to use her new camera – probably because she hasn't read the instructions.

/5

5 Choose the correct options.

0 Jessica (*has eaten*) / *has been eating* the same kind of frozen meal five times this week.
1 Amanda *has known* / *has been knowing* Natalia for about three years now.
2 Lucy *has worried* / *has been worrying* about her hair constantly since we arrived at the party.
3 Actually, I can speak German, so I*'ve understood* / *'ve been understanding* everything you said about me.
4 Nathan *has sung* / *has been singing* the same song all morning. It's driving me crazy!
5 Tom and Ola *have met* / *have been meeting* in secret since their parents told them to stop seeing each other.

/5

6 Read the article and choose the correct answer, A, B or C.

New uniform for city hospital nurses

The nurses of Hallamshire Hospital [0]___ wearing the same old uniform for the last ten years. Recently the hospital decided it was time for a change and today pictures of the nurses' new look are finally up on the hospital website. The [1]___ white and grey uniforms have gone and been replaced by a much more casual outfit. Sophie Baxter, the head nurse on the children's ward said, 'I [2]___ the new look is great. We [3]___ a very long time for a change. The new dark blue trousers [4]___ the dark green tops – they look great together, in fact – and we [5]___ that the colours are much more practical.' Of course, nobody wants to go to hospital, but if you are there, you will now be looked after by some very well-dressed nurses.

	A	B	C
0	A had	(B have been)	C are
1	A relaxed	B creative	C formal
2	A 'm thinking	B have thought	C think
3	A 've been waiting	B 're waiting	C wait
4	A match	B suit	C fit
5	A are all agreeing	B 've all agreeing	C all agree

/5

Total /30

2 JUST DO IT!

2.1 Vocabulary

Sport • Compound nouns • Collocations

SHOW WHAT YOU KNOW

1 Label the sports as *W* for water, *S* for winter or *F* for fighting sports. There is one extra sport.

0 cross-country skiing [S]
1 diving [ ]
2 kayaking [ ]
3 motor racing [ ]
4 ski jumping [ ]
5 snowboarding [ ]
6 scuba diving [ ]
7 surfing [ ]
8 taekwondo [ ]
9 wrestling [ ]

2 Complete the advert with *go, play* or *do*.

SPORTS FOR ALL!

At Abbeydale sports club we offer a wide range of sports and activities. In the main sports hall, club members can [0]*play* basketball, volleyball and five-a-side football. Outdoors, you can [1]________ hockey, cricket, football and rugby. In our fantastic new building we offer the chance to [2]________ judo, karate and kung-fu as well as [3]________ tennis, badminton and table tennis. In the summer, you can [4]________ athletics on the main field and also [5]________ canoeing and sailing on our beautiful lake. We are currently building a pool, so very soon members will be able to [6]________ swimming at the club too.

Contact us at abbeydale_sc@hitmail.com.

WORD STORE 2A
Sport – compound nouns

3 Write the place for each sport in the photos in the last column of the table below. Then complete the other columns.

Verb	Sport	Place
1 ________	________	*athletics track*
2 ________	________	________
3 ________	________	________
4 ________	________	________
5 ________	________	________
6 ________	________	________

4 Choose the word that does not collocate with the word in bold in each group.

1 **squash** *court / bat / racket*
2 **hockey** *track / pitch / stick*
3 **golf** *course / pool / club*
4 **rugby** *ball / resort / pitch*
5 **boxing** *rink / ring / gloves*
6 **cricket** *bat / court / pitch*
7 *motor racing / baseball / athletics* **track**
8 *volleyball / baseball / table tennis* **bat**

WORD STORE 2B
People in sport

5 Complete the interview with the names of people in sport. The first letter of each word is given.

A: Here we are live from the National Stadium and I'm talking to Zoe Striker of Team UK, the new women's 100m sprint champion. Zoe, you are an amazing [0]**a***thlete* and now, finally, champion of the world. How does it feel?

B: Well, I can't quite believe it, actually. I've been training hard with the help of my wonderful [1]**c**________ and the other athletes in the UK team – my fantastic [2]**t**________ . I couldn't have done it without the support of all my [3]**f**________ and all the [4]**s**________ watching and cheering here in the stadium today. I also want to thank the other runners in the race today, my [5]**o**________ , for pushing me to do my absolute best.

A: Thank you, Zoe. The UK is proud of you.

WORD STORE 2C
Sport collocations

6 Read the extract from a radio programme and choose the correct options.

Welcome to *Sports Thoughts* on Radio Sport. This week we'll be asking marathon runner Jeremy Bradshaw what it was like to [1]*come / win / score* first in the London Marathon. We'll talk to Pat Goodhill, who [2]*kept / beat / lost* the national speed-climbing champion and [3]*scored / won / broke* a world-record in last week's UK climbing championships. Skier Daisy Leader will tell us how she [4]*loses / scores / keeps* in shape during the summer and give us some expert advice on [5]*beating / keeping / coming* fit during the winter season. We'll also be asking footballer Alistair Madson what he feels is more important for his career: [6]*scoring / breaking / winning* goals or [7]*beating / winning / breaking* matches. Finally, you'll have the chance to [8]*win / score / keep* a prize in our weekly phone-in competition.

Now, this news just in: U.S. basketball player Dick Boyd amazed fans earlier this evening when he [9]*scored / kept / won* more than 100 points in a single game ...

7 Look at the sports results and complete the sentences with the correct names.

FOOTBALL: United 2 – City 1

0 *United* won the game.
1 ________ beat ________ .
2 ________ lost the game.

TENNIS: WILLIAMS 3 – RADWANSKA 6

3 ________ won the set.
4 ________ beat ________ .
5 ________ lost the set.

ENGLAND 142, SRI LANKA 78

6 ________ won the match.
7 ________ beat ________. 142 runs to 78.
8 ________ won the prize.

WILSON (UK) 3 ROUNDS, TOBIN (USA) 5 ROUNDS

9 ________ won the championship for the USA.
10 ________ lost five rounds.
11 ________ was in better shape than Wilson.

SHOW WHAT YOU'VE LEARNT

8 Choose the correct answer, A, B or C, to complete both sentences in each pair.

1 Now on Channel 6, the __ episode of crime drama *Silent Victim*.
My grandfather played football for Italy in the World Cup __ in 1938; and Italy won!
A last B next C final

2 A top footballer appeared in __ today after attacking a man in a bar last month.
The house has a private tennis __ and an indoor swimming pool.
A trouble B court C racket

3 Swimmer Simon Davies said his main aim this year is to __ his own world record.
You look exhausted, Mike. Let's have a __ at this café.
A break B rest C keep

4 The best way to lose weight is to keep __ and watch what you eat.
The jacket really suited Rachel, but unfortunately, it was the wrong size and didn't __ her.
A shape B fit C healthy

5 Yorkshire won the cricket __ but fans said they played poorly and were very lucky.
You can't wear an orange shirt and red trousers. The colours really don't __ .
A game B pitch C match

6 When Manchester United won the championship last year, their __ went crazy!
It's hot in here. Can you switch on the __ , please?
A spectators B opponents C fans

7 Our hockey team trained three times a week last term and our __ gave us a training programme to do in the gym.
We didn't fly when we went on holiday to Budapest last year. We went by __ .
A train B coach C pitch

9 Choose the correct options.

1 We bought Dad a new golf *course / club / game* for his birthday. He chose it himself at the sports shop.
2 With two minutes of the match left, the fans were screaming at the *player / coach / opponent* to send on another player.
3 The *team-mates / spectators / athletes* had paid £275 each for tickets to watch the game from the VIP area.
4 Mai Lee *won / scored / beat* the favourite Jinjing Ho to become this year's women's table tennis world champion.
5 With five golds in the swimming pool today, China now has more swimmers *champions / players / coaches* than any other country in the competition.

/12

2.2 Grammar

Narrative tenses

SHOW WHAT YOU KNOW

1 Put the events in the correct order to make a story.

Ray didn't finish the race.
☐ She tried to help him get up.
☐ When the ambulance arrived, Lisa and Ray were chatting and laughing.
1 He had only run three miles when he hurt his leg.
☐ When Ray's leg was better, he asked Lisa on a date.
☐ But he couldn't stand because he had hurt his ankle.
☐ Lisa was watching the race when Ray fell over.
Six months later they got married.

2 ★ Complete the sentences with the correct form of the verbs in brackets.

0 The official fired the gun and the race <u>began</u> (begin).
1 It was raining when Ferguson ______________ (crash) his Ferrari.
2 When I reached the 10km sign, the fastest runners ______________ (already/cross) the finishing line.
3 The race began at 4.00 and the last cyclist ______________ (finish) at exactly 5.08.
4 Diane was already at the gym when she realised she ______________ (forget) her towel.
5 Fyfe and Scott ______________ (climb) Everest when the accident happened.

3 ★★ Read the conversations and choose the correct options.

1 A: Right, Jones! It's a yellow card for you.
B: Oh Ref! What [1]*did I do / had I done / was I doing*?
A: I [2]*already blew / had already blown / was already blowing* the whistle three times, Jones, but you carried on playing!

2 A: Did you see the ice hockey last night, Ben? Great goal by Grabic, huh?
B: Well, I [3]*watched / had watched / was watching* the game when the doorbell rang. I went to answer it. It was some sales person, and when I got back, I [4]*missed / had missed / was missing* the goal!
A: No way!

3 A: Arthur, at seventy-six years of age you're the oldest competitor to finish the marathon today. Why [5]*did you decide / had you decided / were you deciding* to run?
B: Oh, well, last year my grandson and I were watching the race on TV when he [6]*asked / had asked / was asking*, 'Granddad, have you ever done that?' I told him that I hadn't run a marathon and he said, 'Maybe you should try.' So, I [7]*did / have done / have been doing* it for my grandson, Timmy. Can I say hello to him? Hello, Timmy!

4 ★★★ Look at the signs and complete the sentences with the correct form of the verbs in brackets.

0 At 8 a.m. the race <u>hadn't started</u> (start).
1 It ___________ (begin) at 9 a.m.
2 At 9.30 a.m. the competitors ___________ (cycle).
3 A: ___________ the (race/finish) at 10.30 a.m.?
B: Yes, it had.

4 When I arrived at 11.30 a.m., the competition ___________ (begin).
5 A: ___________ (it/snow) when you got there?
B: Yes, it was.
6 At exactly 12.45 the last competitor ___________ (jump).
7 By 2 p.m. the crowd ___________ (leave).

SHOW WHAT YOU'VE LEARNT

5 Find and correct the mistakes in the sentences.

0 I ~~played~~ rugby when I broke my arm. <u>was playing</u>
1 We went to the Alps in April, but we couldn't ski because the snow already melted. ___________
2 I watched the race when Hope won the gold medal and broke the world record. ___________
3 Were City beating Arsenal in last night's game? ___________
4 The referee didn't concentrate when Burton touched the ball with his hand. ___________
5 In yesterday's Brazilian Grand Prix, Lewis was finishing in second place. ___________
6 Boxer Joe Foster was fighting over 100 opponents when he retired in 1994. ___________

/6

2.3 Listening language practice

Collocations • Word families

1 Read the text and complete gaps A–E with sentences 1–5.

1 It's something I'm really proud of.
2 Windsurfing became my number one sport thanks to Rachel.
3 I did a lot of different water sports because I grew up near the sea and it was natural.
4 My mum and Rachel are still important role models for me.
5 I first went windsurfing with my mum.

Students' Book recording CD•1.34 MP3•34

Hi! My name's Jackie Smith. I'm here today to tell you about how I [0]*became* the international under-eighteen windsurfing champion at the age of sixteen! [A]*1* I think I've been successful because of two people really. My mum and my cousin Rachel have been my role models.
[B]___ We lived near the sea, and we spent every summer on the beach. My mum had [1]______ windsurfing competitions when she was a teenager. She [2]______ anything but she really enjoyed it. She started to [3]______ me windsurfing as soon as I could swim. I was only about seven years old. My cousin Rachel was there too. She and her family lived near us. My mum gave us lessons together. Rachel's two years older than me and I've always looked up to her. I still do. Rachel was good at everything. She was a really good example for me – I wanted to be sporty like her.
[C]___ At first, windsurfing wasn't my favourite thing. I liked other water sports, like swimming and sailing. I used to [4]______ sailing with Rachel and then we [5]______ a children's sailing club. We [6]______ all our weekends there, even in winter. We did lots of sailing and then we got into rowing. I wasn't sure about rowing at first but my mum thought it was a good idea. Now I'm glad I did it because it made my arms strong, and that helped my windsurfing.
[D]___ She entered a windsurfing competition when she was fifteen – I always wanted to do the same as her so I entered the competition too. She came second and I came fifth! But I really enjoyed myself and that was the moment when I decided that windsurfing was my sport.
[E]___ I think I take after my mum – I hope I have some of the same qualities anyway. And Rachel is like a big sister to me.

2 Complete gaps 1–6 in the text with the correct form of the verbs in the box. There are two extra verbs.

~~become~~ do go join not win play spend teach enter

3 Listen and check your answers to Exercises 1 and 2.

4 Choose the word that does not collocate with the word in bold in each group.

1 **spend** *sports / hours / the weekend*
2 **win** *a competition / a goal / a race*
3 **teach** *a subject / someone the rules / first place*
4 **go** *surfing / aerobics / running*
5 **join** *the gym / a club / athletics*

5 Complete the sentences with the correct form of verbs from Exercise 3.

0 If you want a body like a male model, you'll have to *spend* hours in the gym every week.
1 After Greg finishes studying Sports Science at university, he wants to ______ Physical Education at a secondary school.
2 Sarah didn't buy that snowboard. She ______ a competition and that was the first prize.
3 Hey, can I play too? Will you ______ me the rules?
4 Now that you've spent so much money on trainers, don't you think you should actually ______ running?
5 Most students ______ several clubs during their first weeks at university. It's a good way to meet people.
6 Finally, it has snowed and we are going to ______ the weekend in the mountains. I can't wait!

REMEMBER BETTER

When you learn a new verb or review one you already know, use a dictionary and find nouns that often go with it. Write sentences about yourself or people you know to help you remember these collocations.

Write sentences with the verbs and nouns from Exercise 3.

SPEND

hours *My sister spends hours playing online games.*

WORD STORE 2D

Word families – personal qualities

6 Choose the correct options.

1 Free-climbing, in other words climbing without ropes, is only for the very *courage / courageous*.
2 Training for a marathon takes months and needs great *determination / determined*.
3 David is a very *generous / generosity* guy. He lent me his mountain bike last weekend.
4 I take *inspiration / inspiring* from blind skiers. If they can make it down the mountain, then just about anything is possible.
5 Ryan, you are very *modesty / modest*, but many people say you are the greatest cyclist alive today.
6 Girls, today's performance was fantastic! You showed real *passion / passionate* out there on the pitch.

2.4 Reading

A high school hero • Collocations • Phrasal verbs

Glossary

substitute (n) = in team sports, a player who is sent onto the pitch/court to replace another player who is tired, injured or playing poorly
aim (v) = in sports, to look carefully and choose the place you want to throw or kick a ball, or shoot a weapon
basket (n) = in basketball, the rings at either end of the court; also, the point which is scored when you throw the ball successfully into one of those rings
clip (n) = a short part of a film or television programme that is shown on its own, especially to advertise this film/programme

1 Read the article and choose from the sentences (A–F) the one which fits each gap (1–5). There is one extra sentence.

A Jason's father, David McElwain, fifty-one, said, 'He was really happy on the way home.'
B But he doesn't have time for sports anymore.
C He is also involved in public speaking and is a talented runner.
D However, apart from a couple of minutes in a junior game in 2004, Jason's autism had always stopped him from actually playing in a game.
E Eventually, the clip reached the TV sports channel ESPN and Jason quickly became a national hero.
F When his team-mates passed him the ball, Jason calmly aimed and scored seven baskets from thirteen shots.

2 Read the questions. Find and underline the answers in the article.

1 What is autism?
2 Who gave Jason the opportunity to play in the 'Senior Night' game?
3 At what point did Jason join the game?
4 Which team won the game?
5 Who describes Jason's feelings after the game?
6 What did certain celebrities, film companies and publishers want to do?
7 Which of Jason's other sporting achievements is mentioned in the article?
8 Where does Jason do his charity work?

3 Complete the collocations with the verbs in the box. Use the article to help you. There are two extra verbs.

beat	bring	complete	go	pass
~~play~~	present	raise	score	

0 *play* for a team
1 ______ someone on as a substitute
2 ______ the ball
3 ______ a basket
4 ______ someone with an award
5 ______ money for charity
6 ______ a marathon (or any other race)

REMEMBER BETTER

When you learn a new verb-noun collocation, you can extend your vocabulary knowledge by looking up alternative verbs that go with that noun in a dictionary. Write them as a word web in your notebook with the noun in the centre.

Complete the verbs in the collocations with *ball*. Some letters are given. First, try to do the exercise without using a dictionary or checking online.

0 The best golfers can **h***i***t** the ball incredible distances and with great accuracy.
1 In football, you can't use your hands. You use your feet to **k**_____**k** the ball or you can **h**_____**d** the ball.
2 If the batter **m**_____**s** the ball three times in baseball, then he or she is 'out'.
3 Barnes is a very selfish player. He rarely **p**_____**s** the ball to another player.
4 When I **t**_____**w** the ball to you, try and **c**_____**h** it using both hands.
5 In basketball, you can't just run with the ball. You have to **b**_____**e** it on the floor as you run.
6 Our dog will happily **f**_____**h** a ball or a stick all day long, but it's very hard to get him to **d**_____**p** it once he's got it in his mouth.

WORD STORE 2E
Phrasal verbs

4 Read the interview and choose the correct options.

A: Travis, you [1]*grew up / took up* in the mountains and [2]*took up / set out* skiing at a very young age.

B: That's right. I always [3] *kept up with / looked up to* my dad, who was a great skier and a big inspiration, and it was actually him who taught me and my brother to ski when we were just five years old.

A: That's your twin brother, Nicholas, right?

B: Yeah. Dad used to ski really fast and Nick tried to [4]*keep up with / make our minds up* him. We all skied together for years but unfortunately, in 2008, Dad had a serious accident and had to [5]*set out / give up*. Nick and I were pretty good skiers at this point and we [6]*made up / made our minds up* that we wanted to do it professionally. We [7]*set out / took up* to be the best and we used to [8]*make up / keep up with* new tricks together and encourage each other to try more and more difficult things.

A: And now both of you are in the US national freeskiing team, and were the only twins to compete in last year's winter Olympics.

B: Yeah, and we're both very proud of that.

Autistic boy becomes sporting hero

It sounds like fantasy: an autistic schoolboy is brought onto the basketball court as a last-minute substitute, scores twenty points in four minutes and becomes a national hero. However, in February 2006 that is exactly what happened to seventeen-year-old Jason McElwain from Rochester, New York.

A gift and a promise

Jason has autism, a condition that makes communicating, socialising and reading other people's feelings difficult. However, that did not prevent Coach Jim Johnson from making him 'manager' of Greece Athena High School's basketball team. [1]________ But on the evening of the annual 'Senior Night' game, which was held in the students' final year of high school, the team's coach gave J Mac, as he is called, a shirt with the number 52 on the back and told him he would let him play in the all-important game at some point.

J Mac's magic moment

In the final few minutes, Jason was sent onto the court. [2]________ He scored five points a minute and broke school records. Athena beat their opponents Spencerport 79–43. At the end of the game, spectators carried Jason off the court on their shoulders. His team-mate Rickey Wallace said, 'I knew he could shoot, but I didn't know he could score twenty points.' [3]________ He didn't sleep a lot that night.'

America's new sporting hero

Jason's sporting achievement was filmed and by the evening, a clip of him in action was spreading around the Internet. [4]________ He received offers from celebrities such as basketball hero Earvin 'Magic' Johnson and TV star Oprah Winfrey, as well as film companies and publishers keen to tell his story. Jason even met the American President at the time, George W Bush, who presented him with a special award.

Jason's success continues

Since 2006, Jason has graduated from high school and found part-time work with a well-known food store. He wrote a book, *The Game of My Life,* which was published in 2008 and he now travels across the United States raising money for autism charities. [5]________ In September 2012, he completed his first marathon in fifteenth place, in only three hours, one minute and fourty-one seconds. With all the activity that is going on in his life, Jason admits that he hasn't been playing as much basketball, but says, 'Occasionally, I'll go and shoot baskets.'

2.5 Grammar

Verb patterns

SHOW WHAT YOU KNOW

1 Match verb patterns a–e with sentences 1–5.

a verb + *to*-infinitive
b verb + object + *to*-infinitive
c verb + *-ing*
d modal verb + infinitive without *to*
e verb + object + infinitive without *to*

0 I want to drive a Formula 1 car one day. a
1 We might go for a swim later. ☐
2 The coach makes us run 3km before the training starts. ☐
3 Please remind me to put a clean towel in my gym bag. ☐
4 Karen fancies watching basketball on TV at home. ☐
5 We arranged to meet at the top of the ski-lift at 4 o'clock. ☐

2 ★ Cross out *to* where it is not necessary.

Welcome to the Singapore F1 Grand Prix, where today's race should ~~to~~ be very exciting.

1 We'd like to remind to our viewers that this is a very important race for Sebastian Vettel.
2 Vettel is attempting to win his third race in a row here in Singapore.
3 If the other drivers let him to win again, he'll almost certainly become this year's champion.
4 The weather is wet, so the teams have all decided to start the race with wet-weather tyres.
5 Remember, Vettel only just avoided to crashing during this year's wet Monaco Grand Prix.
6 Vettel's manager has warned him not to drive too fast in these difficult conditions.
7 Keep to watching after the race for more exciting motor racing action here on Turbo Channel.

3 ★★ Complete the texts with the correct form of the verbs in capitals.

1 **RUN**
Shelly tries *to run* every day. She doesn't mind _______ when the weather is good but, she refuses _______ when it's cold and wet.

2 **EAT**
Nick's mum makes him _______ cabbage even though he hates it. She forces him _______ bananas, which he doesn't like, and even though he can't stand _______ seafood, she cooks fish every Friday.

3 **BUY**
Irene could _______ the trainers if she had more money, but she can't afford _______ them at the moment. The sales assistant in the shop advised her _______ them next month because they will probably be cheaper then.

4 ★★★ Complete the second sentence using the word in capitals so that it has a similar meaning to the first.

0 Would you like to play one more game?
FANCY
Do you *fancy playing* one more game?

1 Our PE teacher forces us to run round the hockey field three times before the game.
MAKES
Our PE teacher _______________ round the hockey field three times before the game.

2 Gavin said he would pick us up after the game.
OFFERED
Gavin _______________ after the game.

3 We don't go to judo classes anymore.
STOPPED
We've _______________ to judo classes.

4 Alan really doesn't like losing at badminton.
STAND
Alan can't _______________ at badminton.

5 Come on, team! We must score one more goal.
NEED
Come on, team! We _______________ one more goal.

SHOW WHAT YOU'VE LEARNT

5 Complete the advertisement with the correct form of the verbs in brackets.

Sunny Gym Personal Trainers

Are you trying [0]*to get* (get) fit but not having much success? Are you wasting time [1]_____________ (do) exercises that don't work? You could [2]_____________ (benefit) from the help of a personal trainer. Our trainers will teach you [3]_____________ (exercise) efficiently and effectively, and help you to avoid [4]_____________ (injure) yourself when you work out. Training should [5]_____________ (be) fun, not frustrating. Let our trainers [6]_____________ (show) you the fastest route to success.
Contact Becky at Reception for details and bookings.

/6

2.6 Speaking language practice

Asking for and giving an opinion • Agreeing and disagreeing

1 Complete the phrases with the words in the box. There are two extra words.

absolutely agree kidding
sure thing think true ~~way~~

0 No *way* !
1 The __________ is …
2 That's not __________ .
3 I'm not so __________ about that.
4 I'm sorry, I don't __________ with you.
5 I just don't __________ …

2 Put the conversations in the correct order.

Conversation 1

- [ ] The thing is it gets a bit boring when the same player wins every year.
- [1] Did you hear that Wilson won the tennis again? What do you think?
- [ ] I agree, but nobody is good enough to beat her.
- [ ] That's true. At least not this year.

Conversation 2

- [ ] To be honest, I'd prefer to wait here until we can see again.
- [ ] I can't see anything! Everything is white. It's impossible to ski!
- [ ] Are you kidding? We can't stay here – we'll freeze to death! Come on, follow me.
- [ ] Shall we stop at the restaurant over there?

Conversation 3

- [ ] No way! It's far too cold for running.
- [ ] To be honest, I'd prefer to stay here and watch TV.
- [ ] I'm not so sure about that, but OK. Let's go to the gym instead then.
- [ ] I think we should go for a run.

3 Read the conversations and choose the correct options.

1 A: What do you think about the fact that professional footballers are paid so much money?
B: *To be honest, / No way!* I think it's ridiculous.

2 A: Do you think we will win the next World Cup?
B: *Are you kidding? / That's true.* With our current team we don't have a chance.

3 A: Aerobics is only for women.
B: *That's not true. / I agree.* There are several men in my class.

4 A: Oh come on, referee! That was clearly a foul. Don't you think, Sam?
B: *I'm not convinced. / Absolutely.* It looked OK to me.

5 A: I just don't think we do enough sport at school.
B: *The thing is / I agree* I don't really enjoy sport, so I don't mind.

6 A: Helen thinks motor racing is too dangerous and should be banned.
B: Well, *I agree / if you ask me,* the drivers have a choice, don't they? I mean, they don't have to take part.

7 A: I'm glad they have decided to let girls play in the school football team, aren't you?
B: *Personally, I don't feel strongly one way or another. / Absolutely.* I suppose it's good for the girls who are into football. I'd prefer to go to the gym.

4 Complete the words in the conversation. The first letter of each word is given.

A: Did you see that there's going to be a big boxing match at the new stadium next month? Do you fancy going?

B: Boxing? No, thanks. In my opinion, boxing isn't even a sport. I [0]**t***hink* it's horrible.

A: Really? Well, [1]**I**_____ **s**_____ , I **d**_____ **a**_____ **w**_____ **y**_____ . I think it's really exciting to watch. Boxers are skilled athletes.

B: [2]**A**_____ **y**_____ **k**_____ ? Watching grown men try to kill each other is not what I call exciting! Personally, I don't find violence entertaining.

A: [3]**I**_____ **n**_____ **c**_____ . People have been playing and watching violent sports for thousands of years.

B: [4]**T**_____ **t**_____ , but that doesn't make it right. People have been fighting wars for thousands of years. Do you think war is exciting too?

A: Of course not, but [5]I **d**_____ **t**_____ you can compare boxing to war. For a start, the boxers have a choice. They don't have to fight.

B: Well, [6]**i**_____ **y**_____ **a**_____ **m**_____ , there's always a choice, whether it's boxing or war.

A: Well, perhaps. Hey, how about this – maybe instead of fighting wars, we could put world leaders in the boxing ring. I bet you'd watch that!

2.7 Writing

An article

1 Complete the tips for writing an article with the words in the box. There are two extra words.

end	final	general	how	linkers	reader
sequence	what	~~when~~	who	why	

1 In the first paragraph say where and *when* the events took place and ______ was involved.
2 In the main body, use narrative tenses to describe ______ happened and ______ you felt.
3 Use linkers to describe the events in ______ .
4 In the ______ paragraph say what happened in the ______ and how the people involved felt.
5 Finish with a ______ point, something for the ______ to think about or something about the present or future.

2 Match these examples with the tips in Exercise 1. Each example may go with more than one tip.

0 We were feeling quite tired after an hour or two in the kayak. *2*
a By the end of the holiday, we had had enough of boats and water. ☐
b In the end, we reached the campsite late at night. ☐
c Last summer, my family and I went kayaking in Mazury. ☐
d Unless you are really into kayaking, two days is long enough. ☐
e We hadn't done any training, so our arms really hurt. ☐
f My kayak was full of water and I was freezing cold. ☐
g On the first morning, we set off at 7 a.m. ☐
h My sister was complaining all the time. ☐

3 Complete the linkers in the text. The first letter of each word is given.

Smiles and Miles – an online community for happy runners

discussion board – your injuries

I started running in our local park about eighteen months ago. [0]B*efore* I began, I bought some running shoes and a GPS watch so I could see how far I had run. [1]A______ f______ it was pretty difficult and I couldn't do more than about 3km. [2]A______ two or three weeks of running regularly, it started to get easier and [3]b______ t______ e______ o______ the summer, I was running 10km three times a week.
[4]O______ t______ f______ d______ of the year, I went out for a 'New Year' run in the snow and ice. I was jogging along the road when I slipped and fell and broke my leg! It took more than six months to heal properly. It was really frustrating because I couldn't do any exercise. But [5]e______ , I was strong enough to start running again. I love running, but after my accident, I've decided not to go when there is snow and ice outside.

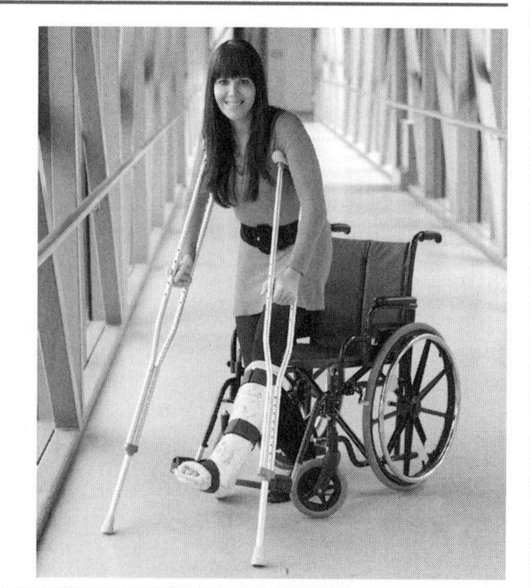

SHOW WHAT YOU'VE LEARNT

4 You have seen this announcement in a magazine.

> Have you been to an interesting event recently? Perhaps it was a charity event, a cultural event, a sporting event, an exhibition or something else! We want to hear about it.
> Write an article about the event for the magazine and we shall give a prize for the best one!

Write your article in 140–190 words.

SHOW THAT YOU'VE CHECKED

In my article:

- I have started by describing where and when the event took place and who was involved. ☐
- I have used narrative tenses to describe events and feelings. ☐
- I have used appropriate linkers to describe events that take place at the beginning, in the middle and at the end of my narrative. ☐
- I have said what happened in the end and how the people involved felt. ☐
- I have finished with a general point, something for the reader to think about or something about the present or future. ☐
- I have checked my spelling and punctuation. ☐
- I have written at least 140 words. ☐

2.8 Use of English

Multiple-choice cloze

1 For questions 1–9, read the article below and decide which answer (A, B, C or D) best fits each gap. There is an example at the beginning.

Football hard man Mario Balotelli is [0]______ for two things: his great skills on the football pitch, of [1]______ , but also for his childish and sometimes mischievous behaviour off the pitch. He has often [2]______ in trouble! But this week, he's in the news because of his softer side [3]______ helping a young boy overcome problems with a school bully.

The teenager asked Balotelli for his autograph outside the striker's training ground. But Balotelli was more interested [4]______ why the young student was missing school. After the child had [5]______ him he was being bullied, Balotelli immediately drove the boy and his mother to the school.

The football star [6]______ to see the headmaster to tell him about the problem. Balotelli then [7]______ with the two boys to help sort out their differences. A source for Balotelli said, 'Mario feels [8]______ about bullying and thinks it's immature. He had no difficulty [9]______ the issue. He felt the boy should not be missing out on school because of bullying.'

	A	B	C	D
0	A hard-working	B easy-going	(C well-known)	D good-looking
1	A which	B interest	C course	D use
2	A found	B had	C known	D been
3	A after	B during	C until	D over
4	A for	B on	C of	D in
5	A told	B said	C reminded	D replied
6	A was demanding	B demanded	C had demanded	D is demanded
7	A made up	B lost out	C called off	D sat down
8	A strongly	B importantly	C powerfully	D terribly
9	A making up	B sorting out	C living in	D going off

TIPS:

Question 1: How would you complete this phrase showing that something is clear or obvious?
Question 2: Which verb collocates with *trouble*?
Question 3: Think carefully about *when* Balotelli was in the news.

Word formation

2 For questions 1–10, read the article below. Use the word given in capitals at the end of some of the lines to form a word that fits in the gap in the same line. There is an example at the beginning.

University student Matt Hebden returned from a once-in-a- [0]*lifetime* trip to Egypt last year having learned how to windsurf. In Matt's case, this [1]__________ was truly remarkable because he suffers from aquaphobia – a fear of water. — LIFE, ACHIEVE

Matt takes up the story: 'I've had a fear of water, [2]__________ deep water, since I was seven. It got so bad that I couldn't even swim in the deep end of the local pool. But I've always been [3]__________ by the sea which gave me the [4]__________ to do something about the fear.' — SPECIAL, FASCINATE, DETERMINE

Matt saw a TV programme about different types of phobias and [5]__________ for him, it included several [6]__________ with people who also suffer from phobias. They all said that it was of maximum [7]__________ not to let fear control your life. So that was when Matt decided to learn how to windsurf. — FORTUNE, DISCUSS, IMPORTANT

The course went well and Matt became close to his trainer, Luke. 'I very much admired how [8]__________ Matt was to try windsurfing,' says Luke. 'Because of his phobia it was often quite [9]__________ for him mentally as sometimes the fear was very strong. It was incredible to watch how he coped with the situation – he was a real [10]__________ to me and to the other students on the course.' — COURAGE, PAIN, INSPIRE

TIPS:

Question 1: You need to add a suffix to form a noun.
Question 2: Add a suffix to form an adverb and make one more spelling change.
Question 3: You only need to add one letter to form an adjective.

2.9 Self-assessment

1 For each learning objective, tick the box that best matches your ability.

☺☺ = I understand and can help a friend.
☺ = I understand and can do it by myself.
☹ = I understand some, but have some questions.
☹☹ = I do not understand.

			☺☺	☺	☹	☹☹	Need help?
2.1	Vocabulary	I can talk about sports.					Students' Book pages 24–25 Word Store page 5 Workbook pages 20–21
2.2	Grammar	I can use narrative tenses.					Students' Book page 26 Workbook page 22
2.3	Listening	I can understand specific detail in a short talk about role models.					Students' Book page 27 Workbook page 23
2.4	Reading	I can understand the main points of an article about a Paralympic athlete.					Students' Book pages 28–29 Workbook pages 24–25
2.5	Grammar	I can recognise and use different verb patterns.					Students' Book page 30 Workbook page 26
2.6	Speaking	I can ask for, give, agree and disagree with an opinion.					Students' Book page 31 Workbook page 27
2.7	Writing	I can write an article about a past event.					Students' Book pages 32–33 Workbook page 28

2 What can you remember from this unit?

New words I learned (the words you most want to remember from this unit)	**Expressions and phrases I liked** (any expressions or phrases you think sound nice, useful or funny)	**English I heard or read outside class** (e.g. from websites, books, adverts, films, music)

2.10 Self-check

1 Complete the sentences with the correct form of the words in the box. There are two extra words.

athlete ~~court~~ fan goal
pitch resort rink track

0 Supporters ran onto the basketball *court* to celebrate with the players at the end of the game.
1 A new ski ________ has opened near here but we can't afford to visit it.
2 Indoor cycle ________ allow races to take place at any time of the year.
3 Artificial or synthetic grass is sometimes used on football ________ in stadiums with roofs because there is not enough light for real grass to grow.
4 Zola Budd, a South African ________ famous in the 1980s, was known for running and training with bare feet.
5 Ryan scored the fastest ________ ever by a player in our team – twelve seconds after the match started!

/5

2 Complete the words in the sentences. Some letters are given.

0 My brother's team is the worst in the group and is currently bottom of the **l***eagu***e**.
1 Our basketball team **c**________**h** says I am one of the best players in the team.
2 Grandad **k**________**s** in shape by going walking.
3 Celia is **d**________**d** to learn to snowboard even if it is a painful process. She refuses to give up.
4 Sebastian is **p**________**e** about judo. He has loved it since he was a child and practises almost every day.
5 Cave diving is only for the very brave. The divers have to be highly skilled and extremely **c**________**s**.

/5

3 Complete the sentences with the correct form of the phrases in the box.

beat my opponent break the world record
~~grow up~~ lose the match make up my mind
score thirty points

0 I know your little brother seems childish now, but don't worry. Everyone *grows up* eventually.
1 Unfortunately, our team ____________________ .
2 We are all hoping that the Polish ski jumper ____________________ today.
3 LeBron James ____________________ for Miami in last night's big game against Los Angeles.
4 Of course, the most important thing is taking part, but I really like to ____________________ as well.
5 When I was twelve, I ____________________ that I wanted to be the best swimmer in the world.

/5

4 Choose the correct options.

0 Unfortunately, we weren't watching when Bolt (won) / *had won / was winning* the 200m race.
1 Chloe finally beat her personal best time because she *trained / had trained / was training* so hard.
2 Dan tried snowboarding when he *went / had gone / was going* to the French Alps.
3 The marathon finally *ended / had ended / was ending* when the last runner crossed the finishing line after almost six hours.
4 Andrew was prepared for the freezing temperatures because he *surfed / had surfed / was surfing* before.
5 Naomi wasn't actually skating when she *hurt / had hurt / was hurting* her foot. She was trying to take her skate off!

/5

5 Complete the sentences with the correct form of the verbs in brackets.

0 If Spain manage *to win* (win) the European Championships, I will buy everyone dinner.
1 I remind my players __________ (not get) angry with the umpire. Shouting and complaining doesn't help.
2 Do you really enjoy __________ (jog) when the temperatures are so high?
3 I think I might __________ (join) the gym again. I've put on so much weight recently.
4 Our PE teacher made the boys __________ (do) aerobics after they said it was easy and only for girls. They were exhausted afterwards.
5 Jenny misses __________ (play) badminton with her sister now that she's gone to university.

/5

6 Read the text and choose the correct answer, A, B or C.

Adzo Kpossi from Togo, in Africa, [0]___ the youngest athlete at the Olympic Games in 2012. When she [1]___ into the water in London to compete in the women's 50m freestyle event, she was just thirteen. In the qualifying race, she [2]___ to Nafissatou Moussa Adamou, a fourteen-year-old from Niger, but beat her own personal best time. Before she arrived in London to represent her country, she [3]___ lots of training at a hotel in Sarawaka, which was the only place in her part of the country with a swimming [4]___ . Kpossi hopes to compete in the next Olympic Games and, after her experience in London, she could [5]___ very well.

	A	B	C
0	A had been	(B was)	C was being
1	A dived	B was diving	C had dived
2	A won	B beat	C lost
3	A has done	B had done	C was doing
4	A track	B rink	C pool
5	A do	B to do	C doing

/5

Total /30

3 GOING PLACES

3.1 Vocabulary

Travel collocations • Compound nouns • Phrasal verbs

SHOW WHAT YOU KNOW

1 Label the forms of transport. The first letter of each word is given.

0 

t*ram*

1 
h______-a______ b______

2 
f________

3 
h________

4 
d______-d______ b______

5 
h________

WORD STORE 3A
Collocations – travel

2 Choose the odd one out in each group.

1 **board** *a ticket / a ship / a ferry / a plane*
2 **book** *a plane / a flight / a hotel room / a ticket*
3 **catch** *a bus / a river / a train / a plane*
4 **cross** *the sights / Europe / the sea / a river*
5 **miss** *a flight / a train / a bus / a hotel room*
6 **reach** *Sydney / your destination / a plane*

3 Read the story and choose the correct options.

Last night I had a very strange dream. I decided to walk to school and at the end of our road I discovered a wide river which I needed to [1]*reach / cross*. A ferry arrived, but when I tried to [2]*board / see* it, the captain told me I hadn't [3]*caught / booked* a ticket, so the only choice was to swim!

I swam for a long time, but I didn't [4]*reach / catch* the other side. I could see a light under the water, so I swam down towards it and the next thing I knew, I was climbing out of a bath in the corner of my classroom! The teacher asked me why I was late, so I told her I'd [5]*missed / boarded* the bus. Very, very strange.

I'm sorry, I'm late. I missed the bus.

WORD STORE 3B
Air travel – compound nouns and verb phrases

4 Complete the advice with the words in the box.

boarding ~~check-in~~ departure gate locker seat belt security

TRAVELFOCUS
Step-by-step guide for first-time flyers

Are you flying for the first time?
Follow our step-by-step guide for a stress-free experience.

Step 1 When you arrive at the airport, go to the [0]*check-in* desk.
Step 2 Check your luggage in and get your [1]________ pass.
Step 3 Go through [2]________. Don't be surprised if the guards search your bag.
Step 4 Wait in the [3]________ lounge. Eat, drink and shop.
Step 5 Go to the [4]________ and board the plane. Don't be late.
Step 6 Put your bag in the overhead [5]________ or under the seat in front of you.
Step 7 Fasten your [6]________. It's time to fly!

5 Put the next stages of a journey in the correct order.

a go through passport control ☐
b the plane lands ☐
c go home or to your hotel ☐
d get off the plane ☐
e the plane takes off *1*
f collect your luggage in the baggage reclaim ☐

WORD STORE 3C

Phrasal verbs – travel

6 Match the phrasal verbs with their meanings.

1 stay over ☐
2 move on ☐
3 go away ☐
4 turn up ☐
5 set off ☐
6 deal with ☐
7 stop over ☐

a take action to solve a problem
b spend the night
c leave one place to go to another on a journey
d arrive unexpectedly
e leave home for a holiday
f begin a journey
g visit someone/somewhere on your way to another place

7 Complete the second sentence so that it has a similar meaning to the first. Use phrasal verbs with the prepositions given in bold.

0 At Ubis Hotel we promise to take action to solve your problem in fifteen minutes or less. **WITH**
At Ubis Hotel we promise to *deal with* your problem in fifteen minutes or less.

1 Dad wants to begin the journey early to avoid the traffic. **OFF**
Dad wants to __________ early to avoid the traffic.

2 Grandma is spending the night at our house, so I'll have to sleep on the sofa again. **OVER**
Grandma is __________ at our house, so I'll have to sleep on the sofa again.

3 After two days in Naples we're ready to leave and go to Capri. **ON**
After two days in Naples, we're ready to __________ to Capri.

4 Ollie's lost luggage finally arrived two days before the end of his holiday. **UP**
Ollie's lost luggage finally __________ two days before the end of his holiday.

5 We are leaving our home for a holiday for two weeks, so the neighbour is coming to water the plants. **AWAY**
We are __________ for two weeks so the neighbour is coming to water the plants.

6 The Walton family are visiting Berlin on their way to Amsterdam. **OVER**
The Walton family are __________ in Berlin on their way to Amsterdam.

REMEMBER THIS

Baggage and *luggage* are synonyms. They are both uncountable nouns.

Please do not leave ~~baggages~~ baggage unattended.
Lost ~~Luggages~~ Luggage Office

If we want to express quantity with these nouns, we use the word *piece*.

Economy class passengers may only travel with two pieces of luggage.

SHOW WHAT YOU'VE LEARNT

8 Read the story and choose the correct answer, A, B or C.

Our 'relaxing' holiday

The trouble started at the airport. We checked in, then [1]___ through security, where they searched my dad's bag and found a pocket knife he'd forgotten about. He explained that it was just a mistake, but the guard was very suspicious. He asked Dad lots of questions and searched our bags again and we almost [2]___ the flight. Mum was not happy.

When we arrived in Vienna, we went to [3]___ our luggage in the baggage reclaim. We waited and waited but our bags didn't arrive. The guy in the office eventually found out that, although we were in Austria, our baggage was in Australia! Mum was really not happy.

We finally [4]___ at the hotel, but we were so late that they had cancelled our [5]___ and are fully booked until tomorrow. Tonight we are [6]___ in a caravan at a campsite next to the hotel. Mum is extremely unhappy.

	A	B	C
1	A got	B crossed	C went
2	A missed	B caught	C boarded
3	A put	B collect	C wait
4	A turned up	B stopped over	C dealt with
5	A terminal	B baggage	C reservation
6	A staying over	B setting off	C going away

9 Find and correct the mistakes in the sentences.

0 I'm sorry, sir. I don't seem to have a ~~reserve~~ for you. *reservation*
1 Please fasten your seat for take-off. __________
2 Our plane is delayed and we've been waiting in this security lounge for hours! __________
3 The GPS said, 'Turn left here. You have caught your destination.' __________
4 Can we go out on holiday for a week in the summer? __________

/10

3.2 Grammar

Present and past speculation

SHOW WHAT YOU KNOW

1 Match the speakers' words 1–3 with the thoughts about the club a–c.

1 It was OK. We danced for a while, then chatted. Not bad, but not great. ☐
2 Awful club. Don't go. Terrible music, expensive drinks and no atmosphere. ☐
3 The music was great. How come I didn't know about this place earlier? ☐

a I'm sure this person liked the club.
b It's possible this person liked the club.
c I'm sure this person didn't like the club.

2 ★ Complete the second sentence with *must, might* or *can't* so that it has a similar meaning to the first.

0 It's possible that's our taxi. That *might* be our taxi.
1 I'm sure that's our plane. That _______ be our plane.
2 I'm sure that isn't our baggage. That _______ be our baggage.
3 It's possible this is the hotel. This _______ be the hotel.
4 I'm sure this is our room. This _______ be our room.
5 We're sure that isn't our bill. That _______ be our bill.

3 ★ Match the evidence with the sentences in Exercise 2.

a I ordered it for 10 o'clock and it's five to ten now. *0*
b It was definitely number 321. ☐
c I think I recognise it from the picture on the website. ☐
d We are flying with Lufthansa, aren't we? ☐
e We certainly didn't order room service five times. ☐
f Our suitcases are blue, not black. ☐

4 ★★ Nick and Anne are at the aquarium. Read their conversation and choose the correct options.

Nick: Look! An octopus.
Anne: Where? I can't see anything.
Nick: Er … well, the sign says there's an octopus, so it [1]*must / couldn't* be here somewhere.
Anne: I suppose it [2]*can't / might* be hiding under that rock.
Nick: Yeah, or it [3]*could / couldn't* be away on holiday.
Anne: On holiday? You [4]*might / can't* be serious! Honestly, I worry about you, Nick.
Nick: It says here that octopuses can change the colour of their skin and totally disappear. Cool! I'd love to be able to do that.
Anne: Nick, sometimes I think that would be a good idea.

5 ★★★ Violet and Daisy are out for a walk. Complete their conversation with the verbs in the box. Sometimes more than one answer is possible.

~~can't have~~	could have	couldn't have
may have	must have	

Violet: Look, a turtle on a fence post! How did that happen?
Daisy: Woah! That's weird. It [0]*can't have* got there on its own. Its legs are so short it [1]_______ climbed up so high.
Violet: There's only one possibility. Someone [2]_______ put it there. What a cruel thing to do!
Daisy: Well, it [3]_______ been a person or I suppose a bird, like an eagle, or something [4]_______ left it there … as a snack for later.
Violet: Urgh, Daisy! That's horrible!
Daisy: Violet, my dear, we all have to eat.

SHOW WHAT YOU'VE LEARNT

6 Choose the correct phrase, A, B or C, which has a similar meaning to the underlined words in each sentence.

1 It is possible we are too late to catch the bus.
A We can't be B We might be C We must be

2 They only set off half an hour ago. I'm sure it's not true that they have arrived already.
A They can't have B They may have C They mustn't have

3 It is possible that Alice brought some sun cream. She's so pale-skinned.
A Alice must have B Alice can't have C Alice could have

4 I'm sure you are tired. We've been walking and sightseeing all day.
A You can't be B You must be C You might be

5 She can't find her passport! I'm sure it's true that she left it in the hotel room.
A She might have B She must have C She can't have

6 It is possible that the plane was delayed because of bad weather.
A The plane may have been
B The plane must have been
C The plane can't have been

/6

3.3 Listening language practice

Functional language • Prepositions • Compound nouns

1 Put the words in the correct order. Then write *R* for something a hotel receptionist would say or *G* for something a hotel guest would say.

0 help / I / you / can?
Can I help you? [R]

1 book / you / online / did?
_______________ [ ]

2 was / thought / I / included / it
_______________ [ ]

3 room / two / booked / a / I've / for / nights / single
_______________ [ ]

4 have / at / special online offer / we / moment / the / a
_______________ [ ]

5 this / fill / can / in / form, / please / you?
_______________ [ ]

6 you / would / breakfast / like?
_______________ [ ]

2 Complete the conversation between a receptionist and a guest with phrases from Exercise 1. Then listen and check.

Extract from Students' Book recording CD•2.7 MP3•50

3

A: Yes, [0]*can I help you* ?
B: Er, yes [1]___________ . My name's Baker. James Baker.
A: Baker. Yes, here you are. Two nights. [2]___________ ?
B: Oh yes, please.
A: That will be an extra £16.
B: Oh [3]___________ .
A: [4]___________ ?
G: Yes, I did.
B: Oh right. [5]___________ . Your first breakfast is free, so you just need to pay for the second day. [6]___________ ?

3 Read the conversation and choose the correct options. Then listen and check.

Extract from Students' Book recording CD•2.7 MP3•50

1

A: So, how was your family cruise?
B: Oh, it was OK. Pretty good, really. We all got on well most [1]*in / of / with* the time. We didn't have any arguments. Well, not [2]*after / by / until* the last day, and then I had a really big argument [3]*with / to / against* my sister. It was stupid, really. I wanted to get [4]*on / from / off* the ship and visit Naples, but my sister was tired and wanted to stay [5]*until / on / in* the ship [6]*by / against / to* the pool. She always does what she wants and she doesn't think [7]*on / to / of* other people. I had to go [8]*to / at / in* Naples [9]*by / on / with* my own with our parents. It was really boring.

4 Complete the expressions in bold in the text with the words in the box. There are two extra words. Then listen and check.

[all part real rest spend sure ~~time~~ trip]

Extract from Students' Book recording CD•2.7 MP3•50

5

It's [0]*time* **to** leave ordinary beach holidays behind and **take a(n)** [1]_____ that you will remember **for the** [2]_____ **of your life.** With Overland Tours you will **see the** [3]_____ **world.** Overland Tours believe that travelling is not only about the destination. The journey is **an important** [4]_____ **of the experience.** Come with us on one of our Overland buses and travel to places other travel companies don't reach. [...] Our tour leaders will take care of you and **make** [5]_____ you have everything you need.

REMEMBER THIS

To help you remember the phrases and expressions you learn, record them in sentences about your own important personal experiences, e.g. your exams.

WORD STORE 3D
Compound nouns – travel

5 Choose the correct options.

1 If it's four hours one way, that's an eight-hour *car / return* journey. Do we have to go so far?
2 The students have suggested that this year's *school / business* trip should be to the mountains.
3 Many travel *agents / leaders* have closed their shops because people prefer booking online these days.
4 TeenTour is looking for teenage tour *guides / companies* to show young visitors around the city this summer. Full training given.
5 Ellen always chooses *beach / skiing* holidays. She likes relaxing and doing nothing.
6 Because of its height, snow is guaranteed all year in the *ski / seaside* resort of Kaprun, Austria.

3.4 Reading

Travelling on my own • Colloquial expressions • Wild animals

1 Read blogs 1–3 and match them with photos A–C.

1 ☐ 2 ☐ 3 ☐

2 Match statements a–d with blogs 1–3. One blog has two matching statements.

In this blog:

a the blogger suggests that he/she won't be updating the blog again. ☐
b it is clear that the blogger is not an experienced traveller. ☐
c the blogger describes two potentially big problems which are solved quickly. ☐
d the blogger mentions that this is not his/her first visit to the country he/she is currently in. ☐

3 Read the blogs again. Are the statements true (T) or false (F)?

1 Jo was very tired when he arrived at his destination. ☐
2 Jo arrived to find that the ATMs in the airport were broken. ☐
3 Alex is enjoying staying with her uncle and aunt. ☐
4 Lucia and Alex will find it hard to understand each other. ☐
5 Adèl feels she has benefited from writing her blog. ☐
6 Adèl is going to visit a friend she made while she was in England. ☐

4 Match the underlined words in the blogs with their definitions.

0 think *reckon*
1 two weeks ____________
2 begin well ____________
3 completely relaxed ____________
4 luxurious or expensive ____________
5 find it difficult to believe ____________

5 Complete the sentences with the correct form of the words in Exercise 4.

0 Katrina *reckons* we'll be in Prague by midday, but in this weather, I think it'll take a bit longer.
1 Jenna's uncle and aunt are really rich, so they always stay in __________ hotels when they go on holiday.
2 Simon and his friends have gone camping for a __________ , so he won't be back until the end of the month.
3 Amy's birthday party __________ when her favourite cousins from Poland turned up unexpectedly.
4 We __________ how much you've grown! How tall are you now?
5 Mum had a massage in the hotel spa. She loved it and was __________ afterwards.

REMEMBER BETTER

Go to the travel blogs section of a site like *TravelPod*. Read some of the blogs and make a note of any useful vocabulary. Don't worry if you don't understand everything. Check new words in a dictionary.

Put the words in the box under an appropriate heading. Use a dictionary if necessary.

après-ski buffet car carriage lift pass piste powder reef return ticket sleeper tank underwater ~~wetsuit~~

Scuba diving in SE Asia	Europe by train	Snowboarding in the Alps
wetsuit		

WORD STORE 3E
Wild animals

6 Complete the crossword. Use a dictionary if necessary.

1 l 2 r 3 o 4 l 5 w 6 b 7 e 8 b

Across

3 a large African bird that can't fly, but can run very fast
7 a large, strong bird which is often the symbol of power
8 a black African animal with long curved horns, similar to a large cow

Down

1 a big golden-brown cat; males have long hair around their neck called a mane
2 a very strong grey animal with thick skin and a long horn on its nose
4 a big cat with yellow fur and black spots
5 a dog-like animal that lives and hunts in big groups; often appears in fairy tales and horror stories
6 grizzly ____ , polar ____ , brown ____ , teddy ____

TravelBlogging

Sign in ▾ 

1

Around the world in six months

Blogger: **Jo** 

Well, my journey didn't get off to a very good start as I lost my passport in Manchester Airport. I panicked, then found it where I was sitting earlier. How stupid! I hope this is not a bad sign for the rest of the trip. The plane was one of those new two-level ones and was really posh inside. It wasn't even half full, so I lay across several seats and managed to get plenty of sleep.

Arrived in Bangkok at 7.00, feeling fresh, but immediately had problems. My card didn't work in any of the ATMs, so I panicked again until I realised that I was using the wrong pin number. Again, pretty stupid. Got a taxi to the hostel, which is great and full of young people like me. I'm writing this in the lounge area. Feeling excited, but also a bit nervous – not really sure how anything works here in Thailand. Please keep reading – hopefully, my travelling (and blogging) skills will improve soon!

2

Summer in Italy

Blogger: **Alex** 

Yesterday I said bye to Mum and Dad and took the plane from Liverpool to Florence, Italy. My cousin Lucia lives here (my English uncle is married to Sabrina, my Italian aunt) and I was very glad to see them waiting for me at the airport. I've been to lots of places, including Italy, before with my parents, but this is my first trip alone and I don't speak any Italian except, *ciao* and *grazie*! Lucia is really cool and she speaks brilliant English (thank goodness!). It's school holidays here too, so we've got lots of time to enjoy ourselves. My uncle and aunt are totally chilled, I've got my own room at their house and the tram stop is just outside. Freedom! Tonight we're going to a party at Lucia's friend's house. I'll blog again tomorrow and tell you all about it – if I don't sleep all day. ;)

3

Old York

Blogger: **Adèl** 

After a fantastic fortnight studying English in beautiful York, it's almost time to head back home to Budapest. Although it was sometimes difficult to find time each day, I reckon that writing this blog has really helped me improve my English.

Tonight is the farewell party organised by the school and all the students in my group will be there. I can't get over how many people I've met from all over the world. Especially cool are Sonata from Lithuania, Marta from Poland and Nico from Italy. We're definitely going to stay in touch and Marta even said she will come and visit me in Budapest. Despite a few problems with accommodation, which we eventually solved, it has been a great experience. I'll miss everyone and I'll even miss writing to you, my patient readers.

A

B

C

3.5 Grammar

used to and *would*

SHOW WHAT YOU KNOW

1 Read the sentences and write *A* for describing an *action* or *S* for describing a *state*.

0 When my dad was young, he went to the Polish seaside every summer. [A]
1 My granddad had a Fiat 126, or 'Maluch'. [ ]
2 Grandma, Granddad, my dad and my uncle all squeezed into the tiny car. [ ]
3 They drove all the way from Wrocław to Sopot. [ ]
4 It took them all night and most of the next day. [ ]
5 Despite the long drive, Dad loved going on holiday in his 'Maluch'. [ ]

2 ★ Rewrite the sentences using *used to*.

0 In the 1990s, people chose very bright colours.
In the 1990s, people *used to choose* very bright colours.
1 Many women wore tight jeans and cowboy boots.
Many women __________ tight jeans and cowboy boots.
2 It was stylish for men to wear white socks.
It __________ stylish for men to wear white socks.
3 Tattoos and body piercings weren't as popular as they are now.
Tattoos and body piercings __________ as popular as they are now.
4 Supermodels such as Cindy Crawford and Claudia Schiffer became famous.
Supermodels such as Cindy Crawford and Claudia Schiffer __________ famous.
5 Was short hair fashionable?
__________ fashionable?

3 ★★ Read the text and replace the underlined verbs with phrases using *used to* or *would*. Use *would* where possible and *used to* if *would* is not possible.

DOWNTHELINE

Advice for teens from twenty-somethings

☞ Tired of advice from mums, dads and teachers three times your age?

☞ Check out our advice from young people just a few years ahead of you on life's long journey.

Reality check, *by Simon Foster, 23*

Five years ago, I thought [0] *used to think* I was going to make lots of money when I left school. I told [1] __________ my parents I'd be the president of a company with a fancy car and a big house by the time I was twenty-one. I believed [2] __________ that companies were going to fight to offer me a job because I was going to be a great innovator like Bill Gates or Steve Jobs. I didn't feel [3] __________ that further study was necessary and I wanted to get a job and start my 'amazing' career as soon as possible. I said [4] __________ that I'd be able to 'do whatever' and 'go wherever' because I'd be so rich and successful. I didn't know [5] __________ much about real life back then.

What would I say to my teenage self now? WAKE UP, MATE! The real world is tough and competitive, and success requires hard work. Take a reality check, work hard and if you are very lucky, success might follow.

4 ★★★ Tick the correct sentence in each pair. Sometimes both sentences are correct.

When we went on family summer holidays:

1 a We used to set off very early in the car. [✓]
b We would set off very early in the car. [ ]
2 a One summer we drove all the way to Spain. [ ]
b One summer we would drive all the way to Spain. [ ]
3 a I used to think it was amazing that Mum and Dad could find the way. [ ]
b I would think it was amazing that Mum and Dad could find the way. [ ]
4 a We wouldn't have GPS in those days. [ ]
b We didn't use to have GPS in those days. [ ]

SHOW WHAT YOU'VE LEARNT

5 Complete the second sentence so that it has a similar meaning to the first. Use the word in capitals.

0 When she was young, Helen didn't get on very well with her cousin Madeline. **USE**
When she was young, Helen *didn't use to get on* very well with her cousin Madeline.
1 I wasn't fair-haired as a baby. **DIDN'T**
I ______________ fair-haired as a baby.
2 Though they shared a bedroom for many years, Tina and her brother Oliver never fell out. **WOULDN'T**
Though they shared a bedroom for many years, Tina and her brother Oliver ______________ .
3 Kim looked up to her team-mate Ellie until she discovered that Ellie was a cheat. **USED**
Kim ______________ her team-mate Ellie, until she discovered that Ellie was a cheat.
4 We hated playing football on cold afternoons. **HATE**
We ______________ playing football on cold afternoons.
5 At every match, the fans started singing at the beginning of the match. **WOULD**
At every match, the fans ______________ singing at the beginning of the match.
6 You thought you'd always be skinny, but now you're sixteen, you're very well-built. **THINK**
You ______________ you'd always be skinny, but now you're sixteen, you're very well-built.

/6

3.6 Speaking language practice

Asking for and giving advice

1 Match the sentence halves. Then write *A* for *asking for advice*, *G* for *giving advice* or *Ac* for *accepting advice*.

1 Can you do	a really helpful.	
2 The first thing	b I would/wouldn't …	
3 Good	c me some advice?	
4 That's	d idea!	
5 If I were you,	e you should do is …	
6 Can you give	f me a big favour?	A

2 Match the questions with the advice.

1 Do you think I need to get them a gift? f
2 What do you think I should wear for the journey? ___
3 Do you think we need to reserve a table? ___
4 What sights do you think we should see in Paris? ___
5 Do you think we should leave a tip? ___
6 Which train should she catch? ___

a No, I don't think you should. The service wasn't very good, was it?
b I think you should. The restaurant is usually very busy on Saturday afternoons.
c Why doesn't she drive? It's much faster than the train.
d I don't know. I've never been. The best thing would be to look online or buy a guidebook.
e It's a good idea to wear something comfortable. We're going to be on the bus for eighteen hours.
f Yes, you ought to buy them something. You're staying at their house for free.

3 Put the words in the correct order to complete the conversations.

Conversation 1

Kim: Mum, 0 *can you do me a big favour* (do / favour / big / can / me / you / a) and help me to decide what to pack for the school trip?

Mum: Of course. Well, I'm pretty sure 1 ______________ (don't / you / to / need) take those high heels, Kim. You are going hiking and camping, right?

Kim: Well, er … yes, 2 ______________________ . (didn't / I / of / think / that)

Conversation 2

Ben: 3 ______________________ (need / think / you / I / do / to) buy medical insurance for the ski trip, Dad? It's expensive.

Dad: Well, can you afford to pay for helicopter rescue and hospital fees?

Ben: Er … not really, no.

Dad: Then 4 ______________________ (were / you, / I / if / I'd) get some insurance.

Ben: OK, 5 ________________ (thinking / good). Can I borrow £50, Dad?

4 Rob is at the travel agent's with his mum and his friend Tom. Complete the words in their conversation. The first letter of each word is given.

Mum: Excuse me. 0 **C***ould* **y***ou* **g***ive* **u***s* **s***ome* **a***dvice*? My son Rob and his friend Tom want to go on holiday on their own this summer.

Agent: I see. Well, boys, 1 **t**____ **f**____ **t**____ **y**____ **s**____ **d**____ **i**____ decide what kind of holiday you would like. 2 **W**____ **d**____ **y**____ have a quick look at our special offers?

Rob: 3 **G**____ **i**____ ! We don't have much money, but maybe a beach holiday.

Tom: Uh huh.

Agent: We have a week in San Antonio, Ibiza for just £249 per person.

Rob: Sounds great!

Mum: Ibiza? I don't think so. Too many parties.

Rob: Mum!

Agent: Er, OK, maybe 4 **t**____ **b**____ **t**____ **w**____ **b**____ **t**____ go on an adventure holiday. We have rafting, hiking and climbing in Austria.

Tom: Uh huh.

Mum: Climbing? I don't think so. Too dangerous.

Rob: Mum!

Agent: Sightseeing in Rome?

Mum: Italy? No way! Crazy drivers.

Rob: Mum! Look, thanks for your advice, it was 5 **r**____ **h**____ , but I think we need to talk about this at home.

Tom: Uh huh.

3.7 Writing

A story

1 Complete the tips for writing a story with the words in the box.

adverbs direct finish narrative short start

1. Make sure you _____ with a sentence that makes the reader want to read more.
2. Use _____ sentences to make the story exciting.
3. Use some _____ to make adjectives stronger.
4. Include some _____ speech so that the story feels real.
5. Use a range of _____ tenses.
6. _____ with an interesting, funny or surprising sentence.

2 Match these examples with the tips in Exercise 1.

a After I had finished reading my magazine, I turned to my dad, who was sitting beside me. ☐
b Well, I certainly hadn't expected that to happen! ☐
c It was five o'clock in the morning and I was fast asleep when something hard fell on my stomach and woke me up. ☐
d 'So, where have you been?' asked my mother. ☐
e Mark was definitely surprised to see me on the train. ☐
f I was wrong! ☐

3 Complete the story with the words in the box.

depressed lengthy loudly overnight really unbelievably unhappily unfortunately

I didn't want to go home. I [1] _____________ didn't want to go home! My holiday in Barbados had been my best holiday ever and I was sitting at the airport, waiting for my flight home, feeling very [2] _____________ . Why couldn't I stay just one more day?

'Passengers for Flight 207 to London, please board now,' a voice came from the loudspeaker. [3] _____________ , I picked up my case and got on the plane behind my parents. [4] _____________ , they were looking forward to getting back. Can you imagine that?

We sat in the plane, waiting to take off for about an hour. People were starting to whisper about the [5] _____________ delay. Then we all heard the pilot's voice: '[6] _____________ , we have some engine trouble and we can't take off this afternoon,' he said. 'We are arranging [7] _____________ accommodation at the Tree Tops Hotel for all passengers.'

I couldn't believe it. 'Yes!' I shouted [8] _____________ . My wish had come true. I had one more day and I was going to stay in the best hotel in the area !

SHOW WHAT YOU'VE LEARNT

4 You have seen this announcement on an international students' website.

Stories about holidays

We want stories about unusual holiday events. Write a story that begins with this sentence:

I shall remember that day for the rest of my life.

Your story must include:

- some unusual weather
- a meeting.

Write your story in 140–190 words.

SHOW THAT YOU'VE CHECKED

In my story:

- I have started with the sentence given. ☐
- I have included the two items given in the task. ☐
- I have included an introductory paragraph to interest the reader. ☐
- I have used strong adjectives to make it exciting. ☐
- I have used a range of narrative tenses. ☐
- I have organised the paragraphs appropriately. ☐
- I have included an interesting ending. ☐
- I have checked my spelling and punctuation. ☐
- I have written at least 140 words. ☐

3.8 Use of English

Multiple-choice cloze

1 For questions 1–10, read the article below and decide which answer (A, B, C or D) best fits each gap. There is an example at the beginning.

Animal criminal

For our honeymoon, we went on an [0]______ tour of the Western United States. One day we decided to go [1]______ in one of the national parks. It was recommended in the [2]______ book as a great place for walking. The landscape around there is totally [3]______ and there's lots of wildlife to spot if you're lucky. We parked in an area of [4]______ forest, overlooking a beautiful valley.

We [5]______ on the walk quite early in the morning and it was starting to get dark by the time we got back to the car. To our horror, we realised that somebody, or something, had broken into the [6]______ car. Our bags had been pulled out and ripped open, and our [7]______ were all over the car park. It was then that we saw the paw prints all over the car and realised who the thief must have been – a hungry bear!

The park [8]______ was very sympathetic and explained that it wasn't the first time that something like this [9]______ happened. Unfortunately, our travel [10]______ company weren't as understanding and said that, because the break-in wasn't committed by a human, they wouldn't pay. It ended up being a very expensive day!

	A	B	C	D
0	A overboard	B overland (circled)	C overall	D overseas
1	A marching	B adventuring	C touring	D trekking
2	A guide	B holiday	C map	D planning
3	A clean	B calm	C unspoilt	D empty
4	A dense	B deep	C solid	D huge
5	A made out	B set off	C picked up	D went along
6	A loan	B borrow	C rent	D hire
7	A belongings	B properties	C contents	D goods
8	A policeman	B attendant	C ranger	D officer
9	A did	B had	C was	D have
10	A money	B operator	C insurance	D agent

TIPS:

Question 1: You're looking for a word that can mean 'going on a long walk'.
Question 2: Think of a word which collocates with *book*.
Question 3: Which of the adjectives best describes the landscape in the story?

Open cloze

2 For questions 1–10, read the article below and think of the word which best fits each gap. Use only one word in each gap. There is an example at the beginning.

The world's most fashionable resort

Where do you think the world's [0]*most* fashionable place would be? Dubai? Thailand, maybe? Well, think again! In a recent survey [1]______ over 1,000 young people, it wasn't the exotic and tropical that finished at the [2]______ of the list, but the cool and mysterious. Reykjavik, Iceland, is now the place where young people would most like to go.

The city, which is one of Europe's [3]______ capitals, with a population of just 120,000, offers an amazing variety of entertainment, from superb restaurants and cafés to cinemas [4]______ you can watch the latest Icelandic and international films. And if you prefer [5]______ activities in the fresh air, take a bus out of the city and within an hour's ride you'll find horse [6]______, fishing and mountain-biking. You can even board one of the many tourist boats and [7]______ a day whale-watching.

The city has a reputation for friendliness that is well-deserved. When you go through passport [8]______ at the airport, the officials are much more likely to share a joke with you [9]______ give you serious looks or ask you difficult questions. So what are you waiting for? [10]______ your seat belt and take off for Reykjavik!

TIPS:

Question 1: You need a preposition here.
Question 2: Where in the list do you think Reykjavik came?
Question 3: You need a superlative adjective here.

3.9 Self-assessment

1 For each learning objective, tick the box that best matches your ability.

☺☺ = I understand and can help a friend.
☺ = I understand and can do it by myself.
☹ = I understand some, but have some questions.
☹☹ = I do not understand.

			☺☺	☺	☹	☹☹	Need help?
3.1	Vocabulary	I can talk about travelling and different means of transport.					Students' Book pages 36–37 Word Store page 7 Workbook pages 32–33
3.2	Grammar	I can speculate about the present and the past.					Students' Book page 38 Workbook page 34
3.3	Listening	I can understand the main points of a conversation.					Students' Book page 39 Workbook page 35
3.4	Reading	I can find specific details in short texts.					Students' Book pages 40–41 Workbook pages 36–37
3.5	Grammar	I can talk about past states and repeated actions.					Students' Book page 42 Workbook page 38
3.6	Speaking	I can ask for and give advice.					Students' Book page 43 Workbook page 39
3.7	Writing	I can write a story.					Students' Book pages 44–45 Workbook page 40

2 What can you remember from this unit?

New words I learned (the words you most want to remember from this unit)	**Expressions and phrases I liked** (any expressions or phrases you think sound nice, useful or funny)	**English I heard or read outside class** (e.g. from websites, books, adverts, films, music)

3.10 Self-check

1 Complete the sentences with the correct form of the words in the box. There are two extra words.

arrive book fasten go (x2) miss ~~reach~~ wait

0 The flight leaves at 1 o'clock, so we should *reach* Prague by half past two.
1 *On the telephone:* Press 1 to ________ a flight. Press 2 to speak to a customer services representative.
2 While you ________ through passport control, please do not use your mobile phone.
3 Dave, I've ________ my train, so I'm afraid I'm going to be late. The next one is in two hours.
4 Let's ________ to the check-in desk and drop off our luggage before we have a coffee.
5 Ladies and gentlemen, we will be landing soon, so please ________ your seat belts.

/5

2 Complete the w,j ords in the sentences. Some letters are given.

0 Before we **b***oarded* the ferry, we parked our car in a car park at the port.
1 The captain has asked you to please **f**_____ your seat belts for landing.
2 We're **s**_____ **o**_____ from home at 5 o'clock tomorrow morning on our journey to Marseilles.
3 Students who want to go on this year's school **t**_____**p** must have a letter of permission from a parent or guardian.
4 At Faraway Travel our travel **a**_____**s** specialise in trips to Southeast Asia. Contact us for details.
5 Today a man was killed by a **r**_____**s** that he was trying to hunt illegally for its valuable horn.

/5

3 Choose the correct answer, A, B or C.

0 Lewis hadn't been invited, but he stayed __ at our place anyway.
A up B on (C over)
1 In this office they __ with 100 pieces of lost luggage each week.
A cope B deal C plan
2 We have been in this resort for a week now. We like it, but tomorrow it's time to __ on to somewhere new.
A go B look C move
3 Do we need to book a table or can we just __ up at the restaurant at about 8 o'clock?
A turn B walk C go
4 Nicole and Ewan are going __ on holiday on Friday for the first time in five years.
A out B away C to
5 Amelia is studying Tourism and when she graduates, she wants to be a tour __ .
A holiday B agent C guide

/5

4 Choose the correct option in the second sentence so that it has a similar meaning to the first.

0 It's possible that we are lost. Do you have a map?
We (*might be*) / *must be* / *can't be* lost.
1 I'm sure these are my mum's keys. They look the same.
These *might be* / *may be* / *must be* my mum's keys.
2 Leo is sure this is not his luggage. His bags are bigger.
This *might not be* / *can't be* / *must not be* Leo's luggage.
3 Jess is sure the light in the sky was not a UFO.
According to Jess, the light in the sky *must have been* / *might have been* / *can't have been* a UFO.
4 It was possible Harry sprayed the graffiti in the toilet.
Harry *must have sprayed* / *could have sprayed* / *can't have sprayed* the graffiti in the toilet.
5 Cindy is sure that Edward forgot to pay for his lunch.
Cindy thinks Edward *might have forgotten* / *can't have forgotten* / *must have forgotten* to pay for his lunch.

/5

5 Find and correct the mistakes in four of the sentences.

0 Before the terrorist attacks on 11 September 2001, airports ~~wouldn't be~~ as secure as they are nowadays. *didn't use to be*
1 On 23 May, my brother used to be born. ____________
2 Would you use to go abroad on holiday when you were little? ____________
3 We didn't use to go camping in the summer. We always stayed in hostels or hotels. ____________
4 I wouldn't love travelling on planes when I was younger, but now I really enjoy it. ____________
5 My friend's father used to was a pilot before he retired. ____________

/5

6 Read the text and choose the correct answer, A, B or C.

The Airbus A380 is the largest plane in the world. The Boeing 747 [1]____ the biggest airliner in the world, but the A380 has around forty percent more space. The A380 carries enough fuel for it to take [2]____ in Dubai and land in Los Angeles without stopping. The journey takes sixteen hours and twenty minutes. In the past, passengers [3]____ have to cope with a lot of noise during journeys, but the A380 is much quieter than other similar planes. A380s are now owned by nine airlines in Europe, Australia, Asia and the Middle East, so if you have set [4]____ on a long flight from any of these regions, it [5]____ have been on an A380.

	A	B	C
1	would be	used to be	used to
2	up	over	off
3	should	would	could
4	off	up	back
5	must	can't	might

/5

Total /30

4 EAT UP

4.1 Vocabulary

Food • Flavours and textures

SHOW WHAT YOU KNOW

1 Choose the odd one out in each group. Then complete the sentences to explain why you chose each word.

0	jam	honey	(rice)	olives
1	carrot	onion	potato	lemon
2	pineapple	cucumber	mango	raspberry
3	milk	biscuits	crisps	spaghetti
4	pumpkin	pear	leek	potato
5	chicken	beef	pork	pasta

0 *Rice* is the odd one out because all the others usually come in *jars* .
1 __________ is the odd one out because all the others are types of __________ .
2 __________ is the odd one out because all the others are types of __________ .
3 __________ is the odd one out because all the others usually come in __________ .
4 __________ is the odd one out because all the others are types of __________ .
5 __________ is the odd one out because all the others are types of __________ .

WORD STORE 4A
Food – fish and vegetables

2 Complete the menu with words for food. Some letters are given.

Dockside Restaurant

All our fish and [0]**s**<u>eafoo</u>**d** is caught fresh each day and cooked to order.

Menu

- Pink Atlantic [1]**pr**_____**s** with lemon, chilli and red [2]**pe**_____**s**
- Wild Pacific [3]**sa**_____**n** salad with spring onions and rich purple [4]**be**_____**t**
- Pan-fried [5]**t**_____**a** steaks with [6]**B**_____**ls sp**_____**s** from our garden
- A selection of [7]**sh**_____**sh** (including crab, langoustines and oysters) served warm with freshly-baked bread
- Grilled Mediterranean [8]**sar**_____**s** with steamed [9]**g**_____**n b**_____**s** and green garden [10]**ca**_____**ge**

WORD STORE 4B
Antonyms – food adjectives

3 Write the opposites.

0 bitter ≠ *sweet* (e.g. sugar)
1 cooked ≠ __________ (e.g. salad)
2 mild ≠ __________ (e.g. chillies)
3 ripe ≠ __________ (e.g. green bananas)
4 fresh ≠ __________ (e.g. bread and cakes)
5 fresh ≠ __________ (e.g. vegetables and meat)
6 fresh ≠ __________ (e.g. milk)

REMEMBER THIS

The words *sweet* and *sour* both have more than one opposite in English.

1 **sweet ≠ bitter** – Examples of bitter foods include *black coffee* and *dark chocolate*.
2 **sweet ≠ sour** – Examples of sour foods include *lemons* and *vinegar*.
3 **fresh ≠ sour** – *Sour* also means 'old' of dairy foods, e.g. *old milk/yoghurt*.

4 Complete the conversations with adjectives from Exercise 3. Use one of the adjectives twice.

1 **A:** Are you ready to order, madam?
B: Yes, er, could I ask you about the Thai Red Curry? Is it _______ ? Chilli gives me stomachache.
A: That's no problem, madam. I can ask the chef to make a _______ version for you without the chilli.

2 **A:** Waiter! I'm not satisfied with this meal at all. First of all, the rice is cold; and worse than that, the fish is completely uncooked – it's _______ ! Are you trying to poison your customers?
B: Sir, are you aware that this is a sushi restaurant?

3 **A:** I love travelling, but it's always great to get home. I'm hungry. What have we got?
B: Er, well, it looks like the electricity went off while we were away. The food in the fridge is not exactly fresh anymore. We've got some _______ potatoes, some _______ milk and there are a few slices of _______ bread.
A: Doesn't sound very tasty. Shall we phone for pizza?

4 **A:** So, what fruit do you eat in Indonesia, Aulia?
B: Well, we eat a lot of mangoes. At this time of year, most of them are yellow and _______ or, in other words, ready to eat. Green ones can be quite _______ tasting, but the yellow ones are exactly the opposite – really _______ and delicious.

WORD STORE 4C

Word families – describing food

5 Complete the table with the noun forms.

Noun	Adjective
0 *crisp*	crispy (e.g. bacon)
1	greasy (e.g. chips)
2	juicy (e.g. oranges)
3	salty (e.g. crisps)
4	smelly (e.g. cheese)
5	tasty (e.g. dish)

6 Complete the sentences with words from Exercise 5. The first letter of each word is given.

0 I don't have time to make freshly-squeezed **j***uice*. It takes so long to clean the machine afterwards.
1 If you cook the salmon at a high temperature, the skin will be brown and **c**_______ .
2 Urgh! You've got **g**_______ from the burger running all down your chin. Gross!
3 The trouble with **s**_______ snacks like crisps and peanuts is that they make you very thirsty.
4 Emma, there is definitely a burning **s**_______ . Did you forget something in the oven?
5 This pizza has a very unusual **t**_______ , Ben. Are you sure you added salt and not sugar by mistake?

7 Complete the word web with examples of food for each adjective.

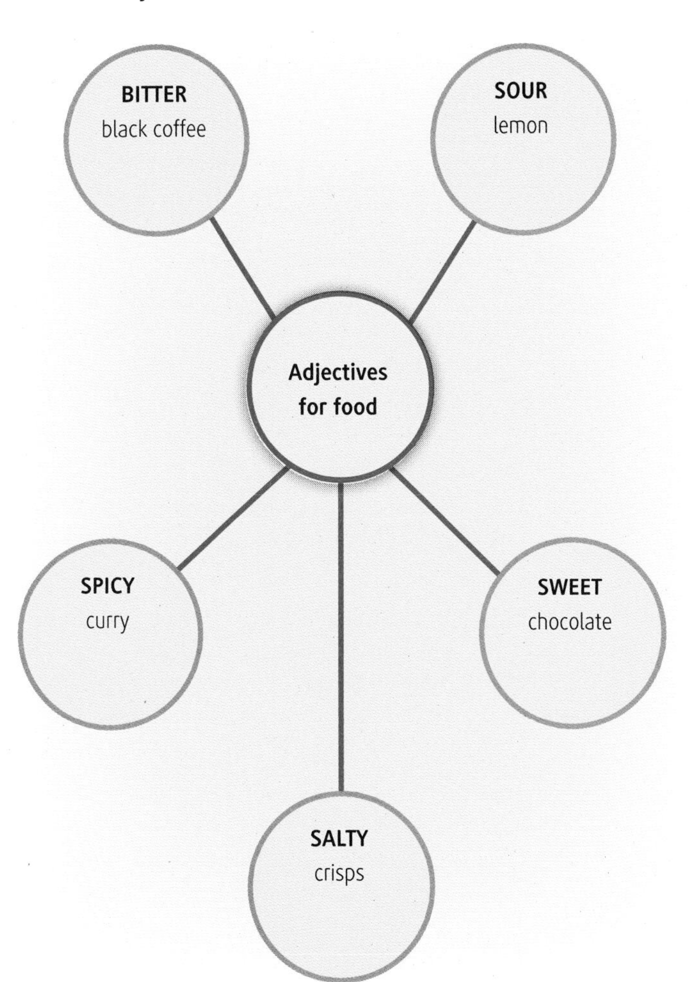

REMEMBER BETTER

Make a list of all the different food you've eaten today. Use a dictionary if necessary. Look at the list before you go to bed tonight and see how many words you can still remember tomorrow morning!

SHOW WHAT YOU'VE LEARNT

8 Choose the correct options.

1 Jackie doesn't like seafood, so she definitely won't be ordering the *prawns / peppers / Brussels sprouts*.
2 Mum, how do I know if this chicken is *stale / ripe / cooked*? It's been in the oven for twenty minutes.
3 I don't mind mild cheese, but I can't stand *raw / bitter / smelly* cheese like the ones with the blue bits.
4 Yellow, red or green and full of vitamin C, *beetroot / potatoes / peppers* come from South America and not the Mediterranean area, as many people assume.
5 Mmm, delicious! How does your dad make simple fish so *tasty / salty / rotten*?
6 Wow! This coffee is extremely *sour / bitter / crispy*. Could you pass the sugar, please?
7 If you eat *juicy / unripe / fresh* fruit, you may get stomachache. Choose softer pieces as they are usually ready to eat.
8 My young brother doesn't eat meat, but he will have fish and he really likes *chicken / tuna / pork*.
9 We aren't eating burgers again, are we? I'm sick of *raw / greasy / ripe* food. Can't we have something healthy for a change?
10 Jess spilled *beetroot / peppers / green beans* all down her white blouse. Her mum washed it three times, but the red stains just turned pink.

/10

4.2 Grammar

Future time clauses

SHOW WHAT YOU KNOW

1 Match the sentence halves. Then underline the main clause in each sentence.

0 If he puts any more chillies in that curry, [f]
1 You'll burn that omelette [ ]
2 If there is too much food tonight, [ ]
3 There won't be any cake left for tomorrow [ ]
4 If you cook dinner, [ ]
5 If we don't take the fish out of the freezer now, [ ]

a if we have another slice now.
b I'll wash up.
c it won't be defrosted in time for dinner.
d if you don't turn the heat down.
e we'll eat what's left tomorrow.
f it'll be too spicy for me.

2 ★ Put the words in the correct order to complete the sentences. Change the form of the verb and add a comma where necessary.

0 dinner / before / clean / Charlotte / I / make / 'll
Before Charlotte makes dinner, I'll clean the kitchen.
1 cake / if / add / sweet / he / too / be / will / any / more
The ______ sugar.
2 we / for / eat / a walk / after / we / go / 'll
______ dinner.
3 sandwiches / 'll / Jason / he / unless / take / be / some
______ hungry.

3 ★★ Read the text and choose the correct options.

Teenchef Easy, tasty and filling dishes for young chefs

Click dish for ingredients and method.

Sticky Fingers Pork
[1]*Until / Before / When* you want to impress your friends, this super-sticky Chinese dish will do the job.

Aztec Chilli
Spice up your life! [5]*Before / After / Until* you eat this Mexican Chilli Con Carne, you'll be as strong as an Aztec warrior.

My-Thai Chicken Curry
[2]*As soon as / As long as / When* you like spicy food, you'll love this mind-blowing recipe. It's hot, hot, hot!

Rasta Pasta
You'll be licking your lips [6]*as long as / unless / as soon as* this delicious Jamaican pasta comes out of the kitchen.

Caveman's Stew
This one-pot stew will keep you full all day long, [3]*until / unless / as long as* you have a dinosaur's appetite!

Big Bad Bolognaise
[7]*Before / After / Unless* you sit down to eat this Italian delight, you'll need to be as hungry as Nero's horse!

Oh So Sweet and Sour Veggies
You won't believe how delicious veggie food can be [4]*until / if / when* you try this awesome Asian special.

Smiling Cow Burgers
Both cows and your friends will be happy [8]*if / unless / before* you choose to make these delicious vegetarian burgers.

4 ★★★ Complete the conversations with the correct form of the verbs in brackets.

1 A: I'*ll help* (help) you cook dinner when I ______ (finish) my homework, Dad.
B: It's OK. Until you ______ (take) your exams, I ______ (do) all the cooking.
2 A: As soon as I ______ (arrive) safely in London, I ______ (text) you.
B: If you ______ (use) Skype, Mum, you ______ (not have to) pay.
3 A: Unless the weather ______ (be) really bad, we ______ (be) there by 9 o'clock.
B: Well, as long as it ______ (not be) foggy or snowy, you ______ (make) it by then.
4 A: Before you ______ (go), I ______ (give) you a piece of cake to take home.
B: Oh, thanks. I ______ (eat) it after I ______ (have) dinner tonight.

SHOW WHAT YOU'VE LEARNT

5 Complete the second sentence so that it has a similar meaning to the first. Add commas where necessary.

0 First I'll lose weight and then I'll buy a new pair of jeans.
Until *I lose weight, I won't buy* a new pair of jeans.
1 We'll eat dinner when we get home.
As soon as ______ dinner.
2 If you don't cook rice for long enough, it won't be soft.
Rice ______ unless ______ for long enough.
3 First we'll do some shopping and then we'll get a coffee.
We ______ after ______ some shopping.
4 When it gets dark, I'll go home.
I ______ until ______ dark.
5 First, I'll check if I can afford the boots and then I'll buy them.
Before ______ the boots, I ______ them.
6 This chocolate will last a long time if you eat one block a day.
As long as you only ______ a long time.

/6

4.3 Listening language practice

Collocations

1 Read what two speakers say about their diet and choose the correct options. Then listen and check.

Extract from Students' Book recording CD•2.22 MP3•65

1

I'm interested in having a natural diet and so for the last two years, I've only [1]*eaten / cooked / used* raw food. I believe that when you [2]*cook / eat / buy* fresh food, you lose the goodness and vitamins in the food. I eat raw vegetables, but of course, I need protein. So I eat raw eggs. [...] I feel healthy and I [3]*feel / have / need* lots of energy, but it's difficult to [4]*stay / live / eat* with the rest of my family and that's a problem.

4

I'm a vegan. That means that I don't eat or [5]*like / use / make* any animal products for any purpose. I don't eat meat, fish, dairy or anything that comes from animals. I don't [6]*wear / make / sell* clothes made from animals either. When I was a child, I ate meat and drank milk like most people. But then, when I was thriteen, I started thinking about where my food came from. I learnt about how animals suffer and I was shocked. I decided to [7]*eat / become / cook* a vegan. [...] I [8]*eat / respect / kill* animals and I don't want them to suffer.

2 Complete gaps 1–4 in the word maps with the verbs in the box. There are two extra verbs. Then complete gaps a–e with the underlined words in Exercise 1.

cook drink eat feel ~~lose~~ respect use

0 *lose* .... [a]*the goodness and vitamins in the food*
.... weight/control/blood
.... your appetite/your memory/your job

1 ______ .... [b]______/nature/the environment
.... somebody's wishes/views/privacy
.... the law/a rule

2 ______ .... spicy/Italian [c]______
.... a meal (for two/three/four)
.... (somebody) breakfast/lunch/dinner __

3 ______ .... [d]______ products
.... chopsticks/a knife and fork/ your hands to eat
.... a computer/phone/machine

4 ______ .... [e]______/happy/fit
.... hungry/thirsty
.... fear/excitement/relief

REMEMBER BETTER

You can record collocations effectively by using word maps. Use different colours for different word forms. Display them somewhere where you will see them every day (e.g. on your mirror, next to your desk) using post-it notes or similar to help you memorise them.

Add three more items to each word map.

1 eat .... meat/vegetables
.... out/in a restaurant
.... ______
.... ______
.... ______

2 have ....
pour (somebody) ....
spill .... a drink
______ ....
______ ....
______ ....

WORD STORE 4D

Collocations – food

3 Complete the adjectives in the article. Some letters are given.

Ace your exams

Eat well, perform well. Today Emma Peel tells us about the relationship between diet and study.

Are your exams coming up soon? Are you studying hard and feeling stressed? In order to do your best, you need to think carefully about what you eat. A [0]**h***ealth***y** diet means a [1]**b**_____**d** diet. To stay energised, eat plenty of [2]**f**_____**h** food and not too much processed or [3]**f**_____**t** food. Why not eat a [4]**v**_____**n** meal now and again to help reduce the amount of meat in your diet? Avoid [5]**h**_____**y** food such as cheese or chocolate cake in the evenings, especially if you are going to sit at your desk and study until late. If you get hungry while revising, choose a [6]**l**_____**t** snack such as fruit, a protein bar or low-fat yoghurt rather than crisps or sweets. Eat [7]**f**_____**g** food such as chocolate, chips, pizzas and burgers only occasionally, perhaps as a reward for a hard-working week rather than as part of your daily diet.

4.4 Reading

Feed your mind • Collocations • Phrasal verbs

Glossary

storage space (n) = space in a house or flat where things can be kept until they are needed
sell-by date (n) = the date stamped on a food product after which it should not be sold
quid (n) = *informal* pound (£) (plural: *quid*, not ~~*quids*~~)

1 Read the article and choose the best title.

a The Uni years ☐
b Ten top tips for student cooks ☐
c Learn to cook ☐

2 Read the article again and choose the correct answer, A, B, C or D.

1 The tips are intended for young people who
A plan to study cooking at college.
B need to cook when they're away.
C want to cook for their families.
D plan to become vegetarians.

2 Before they leave home, students should
A borrow a lot of equipment from their parents.
B buy some new basic recipe books.
C think carefully about what they need to take.
D practise some adventurous meals to cook.

3 Sam Stern advises students to
A spend less money on socialising and more on food.
B shop in supermarkets because it's cheaper.
C avoid vegetarian food because it's expensive.
D try to relax as they cook, even if something goes wrong.

4 When talking about shopping, Sam Stern advises students to
A take turns to buy food with their housemates.
B go to supermarkets early in the day, before the cheaper products are sold.
C look out for cheaper named brands.
D always do their shopping together with a friend.

5 In Sam's opinion, cooking for a lot of people can
A be expensive.
B be a lot of fun.
C make a profit.
D cause a lot of stress.

REMEMBER THIS

To help you decide whether statements are facts or opinions (e.g. question 5 above), note down expressions that are commonly used to introduce opinions:
Many people believe ..., According to X ..., Some people think ..., We felt that ..., In his opinion ...

3 Read the article again and choose from the sentences (1–6) the one which fits each gap (A–E). There is one extra sentence.

1 These can be expensive, but not if you share. ☐
2 For example, a whole chicken is more expensive than pieces, but can make three or four other meals. ☐
3 For the same reason, avoid shopping when you are hungry. ☐
4 If you can't find anyone, follow the recipe carefully. ☐
5 One way is to shop online. ☐
6 I still make mistakes all the time. ☐

4 Match the underlined phrases in the article with their definitions.

0 divide the bill *split the cost*
1 give you more for your money ________
2 a good use of your money ________
3 really change the situation ________
4 take only what you really need ________
5 learn the most important or simplest things about a topic ________

5 Complete the sentences with the phrases in Exercise 4.

0 Shall we share a pizza and salad and *split the cost* ?
1 We have to carry everything that we pack for this hiking trip, so please ________ .
2 Before you try skiing on your own, take some lessons and ________ .
3 Check the price online before you buy. Websites often ________ than shops.
4 If you turn down the heaters in your house, it will ________ to your electricity bills.
5 The juice maker was quite expensive, but ________ . We drink healthy juice almost every morning.

WORD STORE 4E

Phrasal verbs – preparing food

6 Complete the extracts from cookbooks with the correct form of the verbs in the box.

chop cut eat go (x2) ~~throw~~

Don't [0]*throw* the egg whites away. Save them for making an omelette for breakfast tomorrow.

Wash the fish, then [1]________ each filet up into three large pieces and rub with the pepper and spices.

Because there are so few tuna left in our seas, the price has really [2]________ up in the last few years.

[3]________ the chilli up into very small pieces. You don't want a big piece of chilli in your mouth.

You can [4]________ any leftover meat up the next day in a sandwich or as part of a salad.

Just because you are on a diet doesn't mean you have to [5]________ without your favourite food.

Chef Sam Stern, who has been writing about cooking since he was just fourteen, shares his cooking tips for students who are leaving their families soon and heading off to university.

1 Try and learn the basics before you leave home: you will know what recipes work for you and what equipment to take. There probably won't be much storage space in your student kitchen, so only take the essentials.

2 Get someone to cook with you if you haven't cooked before. [A] ___

3 Don't get stressed out if things go wrong; you will learn from it. [B] ___ The skill of a good cook is learning how to correct these mistakes.

4 Give yourself enough time and always read the recipe through before you start. Cooking in a relaxed environment is much easier. I find that listening to music always helps.

5 Look out for good places to shop – butchers' and greengrocers' can often offer better value and taste than supermarkets. They can also give you some great advice for what to do with the cheaper cuts of meat or more unusual vegetables.

6 Remember: vegetarian food is cheap and can be just as tasty. Many of the world's finest cuisines use only a little meat and yet are some of most creative and healthiest.

7 Put your money together with your housemates to create your kitchen store cupboard – herbs, spices, etc. [C] ___ They make a world of difference to the flavour of your meals, so are well worth the investment.

8 Great eating starts with wise shopping. If you make a plan before you head to the supermarket, you'll avoid making impulse buys. [D] ___ Shop at the end of the day as you will find the reduced section full, which means great bargains. Supermarket own brands can be better and cheaper than named brands. Remember to look for the products with the longest sell-by dates too. You can often find them by checking at the back of the shelves.

9 Plan food that will last for more than one meal if you can. [E] ___ A curry or a stew can last for days and is often cheap to make. The freezer is your friend!

10 Cooking with your friends and housemates is not only a great social event but also lets you split the cost. I'm a student, and every Tuesday night we have a dinner party for ten to fifteen people, with each person paying a few quid. As a result, we have wonderful huge roast dinners and lots and lots of laughs.

4.5 Grammar

Future Continuous and Future Perfect

SHOW WHAT YOU KNOW

1 Read the sentences and write *P* for *in progress* or *C* for *completed.*

0 This week he's made breakfast for you three times and dinner twice. C
1 I'm phoning from my car. I've run out of petrol! ☐
2 They've been to the same ski resort seven times. ☐
3 Excuse me, we are waiting for our desserts. Are they coming? ☐
4 I'd only eaten Indian food once before. ☐

2 ★ Read the sentences and write *P* for *in progress at a certain time in the future* or *C* for *completed before a certain time in the future.*

0 The dishwasher will have finished in ten minutes. C
1 We'll be eating seafood on the beach this time tomorrow. ☐
2 While we are eating the main course, the chef will be preparing dessert. ☐
3 Go to the shop now or it will have closed by the time you get there. ☐
4 They'll be baking bread at 5 a.m. ☐
5 Tomorrow morning at this time we'll have arrived in the mountains. ☐

3 ★★ Read the conversations and choose the correct options.

1 **Ryan:** Can I call you again tomorrow at seven?
Meg: No way! I *won't be waking up / won't have woken up* by seven.

2 **Kelly:** Shall I pick you up in half an hour?
Grace: Yes, I *'ll be waiting / 'll have waited* outside the café.

3 **Amelia:** Let's meet outside the school gates at eight.
Jacob: I won't make it. I*'ll be cycling / 'll have cycled* to school at eight.

4 **Mum:** Are you at home, Alex?
Alex: No, I'm leaving school now.
Mum: Well, the courier has a package to deliver. *Will you be arriving / Will you have arrived* home by five?
Alex: Yes, the bus stops right outside at half past four.

5 **Dad:** I'm coming to listen to you sing at eight, right, Emily?
Emily: Dad, I *won't be singing / won't have sung* at eight. The concert finishes at seven.

6 **Ethan:** *Will you be leaving at / Will you have left* by half past nine?
Paige: Oh definitely. I'm tired and I want to be home by eight at the latest.
Ethan: So, I won't see you because I can't be there till half past nine.

4 ★★★ Complete the sentences with the Future Continuous or Future Perfect form of the verbs in bold in the list.

Start dinner @ 11:00
*11.00 **put** pork in oven*
*12.45 **peel** potatoes and carrots*
*13.00 **wash** Brussels sprouts*
*13.30 **boil** vegetables*
*14.00 **serve** dinner*
*15.00 **sleep** in front of the TV ☺*

0 By 11.05 we *'ll have put* the pork in the oven.
1 At 10.30 we __________ dinner yet.
2 We __________ the potatoes and carrots at 12.45.
3 By 13.30 we __________ the Brussels sprouts.
4 We __________ the vegetables by 13.55.
5 We __________ dinner at 14.00.
6 At 15.05 we __________ in front of the TV.

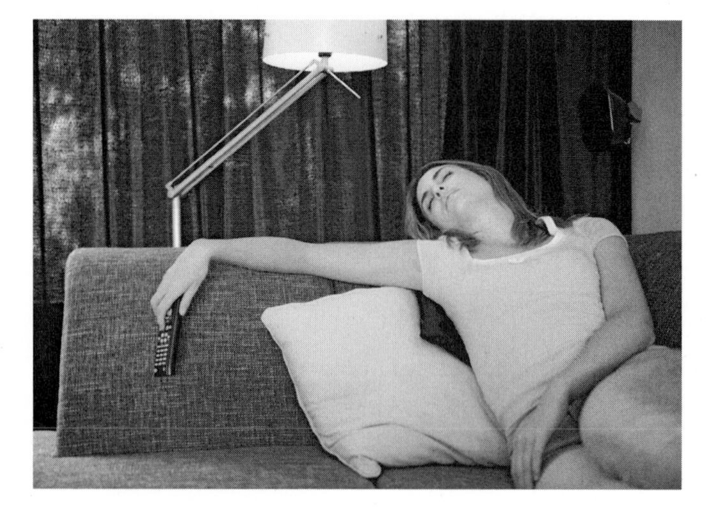

SHOW WHAT YOU'VE LEARNT

5 Complete the sentences with the Future Continuous or Future Perfect form of the verbs in brackets. Use short forms where possible.

1 I can't meet you at six tomorrow because I __________ (not finish) my homework.
2 Dad __________ (wait) for you outside the school at 4 o'clock. Don't be late!
3 __________ (he/finish) that book he's reading by the end of the year?
4 Sorry, but by the time you get home, I __________ (eat) all the chocolates!
5 __________ (we/sunbathe) next to the pool at this time next week?
6 This time next year she __________ (study) law at Cambridge University.

/6

4.6 Speaking language practice

In a restaurant

1 Complete the restaurant phrases with *Can I* or *Do you*. Then write *W* for something the waiter would say or *C* for something the customer would say.

0 Could I have the bill, please? [C]
1 What __________ get for you? [ ]
2 __________ know what the pasta sauce is? [ ]
3 __________ have chips with that? [ ]
4 __________ have any vegetarian dishes? [ ]
5 __________ order, please? [ ]
6 __________ take your order? [ ]

2 Put the words in the correct order to form sentences.

0 you / what / special / know / do / today's / is?
Do you know what today's special is?

1 **A:** about / fish / what?
____

B: salmon / is / the / delicious
____

2 tell / what / can / you / the Chef's Special Lamb / me / is?
____

3 me / you / the Farmer's Lunch / what / is / tell / could?
____

4 **A:** about / the Diavolo Pizza / how?
____

B: very / spicy / it's
____

5 know / there / olives / I'd / in / the pasta / like / if / to / are
____

6 get / can / I / where / the best pizza?
____

3 Cross out one unnecessary word in six of the questions.

0 I'd like to know what seafood ~~do~~ you have.
1 Do you know what time does the restaurant closes?
2 I'd like to see the dessert menu, please.
3 Can you tell me how long it will it take to prepare the duck?
4 Could you tell me what is the vegetarian special is?
5 I'd like to know if do you have a table for two at 8 o'clock this evening.
6 Can you tell me what soups do you have?
7 Could you tell me where the gentlemen's toilets are?
8 Do you know if is the chicken curry is very spicy?

4 Complete the words in the conversation. The first letter of each word is given.

A: Excuse me, waiter. 0**C**an **I** **o**rder, please?
B: Good evening, sir. Certainly, what can I get for you?
A: 1**C**____ **y**____ **t**____ **m**____ **w**____ **t**____ special **i**____ ?
B: Yes, sir. This evening's special is roast beef.
A: Oh no! I don't eat red meat. I'll have chips, please. But 2**c**____ **I** **h**____ them cold?
B: Cold chips? Er, well, certainly, sir. A large portion?
A: Yes, that 3**s**____ **g**____ . Large, please.
B: Perhaps you'd like some vegetables with your chips?
A: I'm 4**s**____ , but I'm **a**____ to vegetables. They make me cough.
B: Cough? Of course, sir. Is that everything?
A: 5**D**____ **y**____ **h**____ **a**____ fruit salad?
B: Er, I'll check with the chef. So, that's cold chips, followed by fruit salad for dessert.
A: No, fruit salad with the chips, please.
B: With the …? Er, whatever you want, sir. And to drink?
A: Just tap water, please. But I'll have it warm.
B: Warm? Well, er, of course, sir.
A: And 6**c**____ **I** **s**____ the dessert menu, please?
B: Certainly, sir. Perhaps you'd like some hot ice cream with sardines?
A: Don't be ridiculous! What kind of restaurant is this?
B: Sorry, sir. It's just that your order is rather … unusual.
A: Well, I know what I like and I like what I know and you, young man, will definitely not be getting a tip!

Cold chips, fruit salad and a glass of warm water, sir. Enjoy your meal.

4.7 Writing

A semi-formal email

1 Complete the tips for writing a semi-formal email with the words in the box. There are two extra words.

clarification indirect informal polite ~~politely~~ reason refer reply responding why write

1 Start the email *politely*.
2 Don't use abbreviations, ________ phrases or contractions.
3 In the first paragraph, ________ to the letter/email/ advert you are ________ to (if appropriate).
4 Also in the first paragraph, say ________ you are writing.
5 In the main body, use ________ expressions (e.g. ________ questions) to ask for information.
6 If something is unclear, ask for ________ .
7 In the final paragraph, mention that you would like a ________ .

2 Match 1–6 with a–g to make phrases. Then match the phrases with the tips in Exercise 1.

0 Dear Sir/	a questions I would like to ask.	1
1 Could you clarify how much	b in the local newspaper.	☐
2 There are several	c some information about your offer.	☐
3 I look forward to	d discount you offer to groups?	☐
4 I am writing to ask for	e receiving your reply soon.	☐
5 I saw your advert	f which activities the centre offers.	☐
6 I would like to know	g Madam,	☐

3 Complete the words in the email. The first letter of each word is given.

D*ear* Mr Mckinney,

[1]T_____ y_____ f_____ y_____ email r_____ the training courses offered by your organisation. I [2]a_____ w_____ to e_____ a_____ the Level 1 course in food hygiene.

First of all, [3]c_____ I a_____ a_____ the possibility of studying this course part-time rather than full-time? I am still at school and so can only study in the evenings or at weekends. If a part-time course is available, [4]c_____ y_____ c_____ w_____ the price is the same as for a full-time course? I [5]w_____ a_____ l_____ to a_____ i_____ your organisation runs this course during the summer holidays. This would be an ideal option for students such as myself.

I [6]l_____ f_____ to r_____ y_____ r_____ soon.

Yours sincerely,
Oliver Thornber

SHOW WHAT YOU'VE LEARNT

4 You recently received an email from your English friend Kelly. Read part of her email and the advert below and write your email to the centre.

I know you're looking for somewhere to have your birthday. I saw this advert and thought you might be interested. Why don't you write to them, tell them about your birthday and ask for some more information? Could be good!

Love,
Kelly

Are you looking for an original birthday party idea?

Do you love the great outdoors?

Are you a big fan of BBQ food?

Why not have your birthday party at High Grange Outdoor Activity Centre? We can offer a fun-filled day of outdoor activities, followed by a fantastic BBQ dinner in our gorgeous garden. We offer big discounts for large groups. Email us now for more information at H_G_O_A_C@dmail.com.

Write your email in 140–190 words.

SHOW THAT YOU'VE CHECKED

In my semi-formal email:

- I have started with an appropriate polite greeting. ☐
- I have mentioned the letter/email/advert I received or saw in the first paragraph. ☐
- I have given a reason for writing. ☐
- I have politely asked for information and clarification (e.g. with indirect questions). ☐
- I have made it clear that I would like the person to reply to my email in the final paragraph. ☐
- I have ended with an appropriate phrase (*Yours faithfully/sincerely*). ☐
- I have checked my spelling and punctuation. ☐
- I have written at least 140 words. ☐

4.8 Use of English

Word formation

1 For questions 1–9, read the article below. Use the word given in capitals at the end of some of the lines to form a word that fits in the gap in the same line. There is an example at the beginning.

Superfoods

In recent years we have seen the appearance of 'superfoods' in the media. These are foods that are	
supposed to be especially [0] *healthy* , for example, garlic, blueberries and broccoli. But is there any	HEALTH
[1] __________ evidence that they are as good for us as many people say? Let's take a look at the	SCIENCE
opinion of leading [2] __________ , Dr Edward Collins.	NUTRITION
'Superfoods are definitely good for us. But many people often [3] __________ the term and think	UNDERSTAND
that eating just these foods will prevent diseases or make them live longer. This is not true, of course.	
Everyone needs a [4] __________ diet, not just to eat three or four things. This is especially true for	BALANCE
[5] __________ , whose diet is already restricted because they don't eat meat. So the message is to eat	VEGETABLE
a [6] __________ of foods, including, but not limited to, superfoods.	MIX
Also, if you're suddenly going to eat a lot of a certain type of food, check you're not [7] __________ to	ALLERGY
it first – even superfoods are not good for everyone! The usual rules of sensible eating apply to	
superfoods too. Don't eat a lot of tinned or [8] __________ products – fresh food is always better.	FREEZE
And try and eat something at each meal that's good for you but that is also [9] __________ so that you	FILL
don't snack between meals.'	

TIPS:

Question 1: You need an adjective here.
Question 2: What is Dr Collins' job title?
Question 3: Read this sentence and the next one to get the full meaning.

Key word transformations

2 For questions 1–6, complete the second sentence so that it has a similar meaning to the first sentence, using the word given. Do not change the word given. You must use between two and five words, including the word given. There is an example.

0 Breakfast, lunch and dinner are all equally important.
AS
Breakfast is just *as important as* lunch and dinner.

1 Paulo wasn't hungry, so he didn't have any dinner.
WENT
Paulo __________ he wasn't hungry.

2 When you've finished your peas, you can have cake.
UNTIL
You __________ you've finished your peas.

3 We can listen to a live band playing during the meal tonight.
WILL
A live band __________ we are eating our meal tonight.

4 What clothes do I need to wear to work as a waiter?
TELL
Can __________ clothes I need to wear to work as a waiter?

5 Jack's going to finish the cookery course before he goes back to school.
HAVE
The cookery course __________ by the time Jack goes back to school.

6 If people eat a balanced diet, they usually get enough vitamins.
AS
People usually get enough vitamins __________ a balanced diet.

TIPS:

Question 1: You need a phrasal verb which means 'not have something'.
Question 2: You need to make a verb negative to keep the same meaning.
Question 3: Which future form do you need here?

4.9 Self-assessment

1 For each learning objective, tick the box that best matches your ability.

☺☺ = I understand and can help a friend.
☺ = I understand and can do it by myself.
☹ = I understand some, but have some questions.
☹☹ = I do not understand.

			☺☺	☺	☹	☹☹	Need help?
4.1	Vocabulary	I can describe food that I like and don't like.					Students' Book pages 48–49 Word Store page 9 Workbook pages 44–45
4.2	Grammar	I can use future time clauses to talk about future plans, predictions and conditions.					Students' Book page 50 Workbook page 46
4.3	Listening	I can understand the main points of a short monologue.					Students' Book page 51 Workbook page 47
4.4	Reading	I can understand the main points of an article.					Students' Book pages 52–53 Workbook pages 48–49
4.5	Grammar	I can talk about future actions and when they will happen.					Students' Book page 54 Workbook page 50
4.6	Speaking	I can order food in a restaurant and ask for information politely.					Students' Book page 55 Workbook page 51
4.7	Writing	I can write a semi-formal email.					Students' Book pages 56–57 Workbook page 52

2 What can you remember from this unit?

New words I learned (the words you most want to remember from this unit)	**Expressions and phrases I liked** (any expressions or phrases you think sound nice, useful or funny)	**English I heard or read outside class** (e.g. from websites, books, adverts, films, music)

4.10 Self-check

1 Complete the sentences with the opposites of the words in brackets. The last letter of each word is given.

0 Make sure you choose a ripe (unripe) mango. They aren't good if they're not ready.
1 Eurgh! I just drank a big mouthful of _______r (fresh) milk. I think I'm going to be sick!
2 A _______d (monotonous) diet can include some sweet or greasy food, just not too much.
3 Bring that _______e (fresh) bread with us to the park. We'll feed the ducks.
4 This salad dressing is a bit too _______y (tasteless). Let's add some more honey and lime juice.
5 I'm afraid I overcooked the pork and now it's rather _______y (juicy). Sorry everyone.

/5

2 Complete the sentences with the words in the box. There are two extra words.

away chop food ~~healthy~~
mild smelly snack without

0 The best way to stay fit is to do plenty of exercise and have a healthy diet.
1 Don't have a big meal if you're not hungry. Have a light _______ instead.
2 Will you _______ up some peppers and some carrots so we can dip them in this hummus?
3 For me, the hardest part of being on a diet is going _______ chocolate.
4 Mum won't let me take egg sandwiches to school. She says they are too _______ .
5 The problem with the school snack shop is that they don't sell any fresh _______ . It's just crisps, chocolate and nuts.

/5

3 Complete the words in the sentences. The first two letters of each word are given.

0 I've bought some lovely ripe oranges and I'm going to make some fresh juice. Would you like a glass?
1 I can't stand **pr**_______ . They are like insects that live in the sea – all those legs and those horrible black eyes! How can you eat them?
2 English breakfast is very **gr**_______ if you fry everything. I prefer to grill the bacon and have scrambled eggs. It's much healthier that way.
3 Choose the lettuce carefully. I want a fresh, **cr**_______ green salad with no brown bits or soft lettuce leaves.
4 Our Atlantic Pizza is made with crab meat and tuna, and is ideal for lovers of **se**_______ .
5 The only types of **sh**_______ I like are langoustines and crab. I can't stand oysters.

/5

4 Choose the correct answer, A, B or C.

0 I know you're hungry. I promise we'll go for a burger __ we get into town, OK?
(A) as soon as B until C unless
1 Candidates must not leave the exam room __ the teacher gives them permission.
A when B if C unless
2 I'll switch the washing machine on __ Kate has had a shower.
A as long as B when C unless
3 __ you ask someone what to do, you'll never know.
A If B Unless C After
4 Miko can go to the party __ she's home by midnight.
A before B as soon as C as long as
5 Tim will write the Christmas cards __ you find out everyone's address.
A if B until C unless

/5

5 Complete the sentences with the Future Simple, Future Perfect Simple or Future Continuous form of the verbs in brackets.

0 Tomorrow at this time we will be sitting (sit) in the exam hall.
1 We predict the price of computer games _____ (go down) by the end of the year.
2 One day I think you _____ (like) strong flavours such as blue cheese. Your tastes change as you get older.
3 Tomorrow Uncle Mark _____ (go without) cigarettes for four years.
4 Mum _____ (not work) this Saturday morning, so we are going shopping together.
5 _____ (you/finish) that book by the time we go on holiday? I'd like to read it while we're away.

/5

6 Read the text and choose the correct answer, A, B or C.

We're going on holiday tomorrow, so we need to sort the fridge out. Actually, this milk is already [0]__ , so we can throw it [1]__ . This cabbage will [2]__ bad by the time we get back and we're probably not going to eat the rest of this ham [3]__ we have it for breakfast tomorrow. The chicken should be OK, [4]__ we freeze it today, but that cheese your grandma gave us already [5]__ a bit strange. I think it will have to go too. What a waste of food!

0 A rotten (B) sour C stale
1 A up B off C away
2 A have gone B be going C go
3 A unless B until C if
4 A when B as long as C as soon as
5 A smelly B smells C is smelling

/5

Total /30

5 ONE WORLD

5.1 Vocabulary

Natural world • Verb collocations

SHOW WHAT YOU KNOW

1 Complete the forum posts with words for geographical features.

survivingschool.net Location, location, location

Do you go to school in an unusual place or make an unusual journey to get there? If so, tell us about it below.

Julia_D$ I go to an international school on the other side of Tokyo. Tokyo is a huge [0]*city* and I have to catch a train, then the underground, then a bus to get to school. It takes nearly two hours and I hate it. ☹ ▭

Sonia_16 My family lives on a very small [1]_______ , so I get a boat every day to get to school. I can't be late because there's only one boat in the morning. ▭

Bret@home Australia is a huge [2]_______ and my parents own a farm hundreds of kilometres from the nearest big town. There's no secondary school in our little community, so I have all my lessons online. ▭

pinky I go to school near Cape Town in South Africa and about 20km from my school is the point where two [3]_______ meet – the Atlantic and the Indian. I think our school has the most beautiful location in the world. ▭

8ball_16 I go to school in Istanbul, which is famous for being the only city in the world where two [4]_______ meet. My school is in Asia, but when I look out of the window, I can see Europe. ▭

hellokaty_14 Everyone has heard of the famous [5]_______ in our city, but most people don't know that the city is also called Niagara Falls. In fact, my school is called Niagara Falls High School! ▭

Kid_16 My family lives in Dubai, very close to the [6]_______ . It hardly ever rains, but we regularly have storms – sand storms! When that happens we have to stay indoors, so it's impossible to get to school. ▭

Yoda_347 My parents own a restaurant high in the [7]_______ and I have to get a cable car down to the town to get to school every day. Sometimes, if it's really windy, I just have to stay at home ;) ▭

WORD STORE 5A
Geographical features

2 Complete the extracts from travel guides with the correct form of the words in the box. There are two extra words.

~~bank~~	bay	coast	dam	foothill
glacier	peninsula	river	sea	valley

Fishing fans can find a quiet spot to enjoy their hobby on the beautiful [0]*banks* of the River Mure.

New Zealand's [1]_______ are an absolute must for any visitor, but you need good boots and an ice axe to climb them.

For walkers who don't wish to climb to the highest peaks of the Himalayas, the lower [2]_______ are an ideal destination.

The Isle of Harris off Scotland's west [3]_______ has wonderful sandy beaches.

The Peak District in the north of England has several large man-made [4]_______ which help to control the water supply to nearby towns and villages.

Down in the [5]_______ between the hills, is the beautiful village of Grindleford.

A walk along the [6]_______ provides wonderful views of the ocean on three sides.

The water in the [7]_______ is colder than the river, but warmer than the sea.

REMEMBER BETTER

To help you remember these and other geographical features, think of examples you know from your country or from other countries you have visited and write them next to the words, e.g. the Baltic Sea.

WORD STORE 5B
Verb collocations

3 Choose the correct options.

1 On our second day in Barcelona we caught the cable car to the top of Montjuic, the hill that *strikes / overlooks* the city.
2 The River Thames *flows / floods* through the south of England and the heart of London.
3 Scientists warn that a huge earthquake may *strike / erupt* soon in British Columbia, Canada.
4 In 1997 the River Odra *flooded / burst* Wrocław in Poland and left around one-third of the city centre underwater.
5 When the Indonesian volcano Krakatoa *burst / erupted* in 1883, it made the loudest sound ever in history.
6 When the Amazon River *bursts / floods* its banks, the floods are truly enormous.

WORD STORE 5C
Word families

4 Complete the table.

	Noun	Verb
0	destruction	destroy
1	________	evacuate
2	________	locate
3	________	predict
4	________	produce
5	________	reduce

5 Complete the sentences with the correct form of words from Exercise 4.

0 a The town was completely destroyed by a huge earthquake in 1765.
b Nothing good comes from war. Only death and destruction.
1 a We have a big ________ on the price of shoes in our winter sale.
b Don't miss our one-day sale. Everything will be ________ by fifty percent.
2 a In case of a fire, ________ the building using the emergency exits.
b The ________ of the area around the volcano is now complete.
3 a My new school is ________ on the banks of a beautiful river.
b The new sports centre has excellent facilities, but the ________ is terrible. It's miles away!
4 a ________ of Coolfresh bottled water is moving from France to Poland.
b We ________ four different models of ski jackets. They cost from €100 to €425.
5 a It's impossible to ________ exactly where and when lightning will strike.
b Most mobile phones have text ________ . It's the function that guesses what word you are going to type next, to make it easier to write messages quickly.

SHOW WHAT YOU'VE LEARNT

6 Choose the correct answer, A, B or C.

1 Protesters say that building a new ___ will destroy an area of unique natural beauty.
A sea B peninsula C dam
2 We aren't staying up on the mountain. We're in a hostel down in the bottom of the ___ .
A bank B valley C bay
3 Kim loves living on the ___ because she likes the beach.
A coast B foothills C glacier
4 We're very lucky because our flat ___ the local park.
A floods B destroys C overlooks
5 After heavy rain, the water in the river ___ very quickly.
A flows B strikes C erupts
6 The ___ of rainforests leads to the loss of many species of plants and animals.
A destruction B evacuation C location
7 Scientists are working on a new way to ___ when typhoons could strike.
A produce B predict C reduce
8 Think carefully about ___ before you choose a student house. It's best to be close to the university.
A reduction B location C prediction
9 The ___ of children from London during the Second World War took many months.
A destruction B reduction C evacuation
10 Scientists say that the ___ in the size of the ice sheet over Antarctica is because of climate change.
A reduction B production C location

/10

5.2 Grammar

Articles: no article, *a/an* or *the*

SHOW WHAT YOU KNOW

1 Read the text and choose the correct options.

Visit Poland: Polish weather
Some people say [1]Ø / *the* Polish people love talking about [2]*a* / *the* weather. This is no surprise because Poland is [3]*a* / *an* relatively small country, but it has [4]*a* / *an* interesting and very diverse climate. For example, when [5]*the* / *a* sun is shining in Silesia, in March, [6]*the* / Ø lakes of Suwałki, are often still covered with [7]*an* / Ø ice. On average, Suwałki is [8]*the* / *a* coldest place in Poland, where [9]*the* / *a* local people cope with winter temperatures of minus twenty to minus thirty degrees. So if you meet a Polish person in [10]*a* / *the* lift somewhere and [11]*a* / *the* lift gets stuck, now you can say something about Polish weather!

2 ★ Cross out *the* where it's not necessary. One sentence is correct.

0 The government should spend more on ~~the~~ education and less on ~~the~~ defence.
1 Has Emilia visited the Netherlands and the Germany?
2 In January 2013 only around thirty-nine percent of people in the United States owned the passports.
3 The population of the Estonia is about 1.3 million.
4 The citizens of Germany chose a female Prime Minister, and naturally the Prime Minister has promised to do more for the women of her country.
5 The biggest city in the China is the Shanghai. Around 16 million people live there.
6 The pollution is generally a problem in big cities, but the pollution in this city is worse than in most others.

3 ★★ Complete the protest signs with *a/an*, *the* or Ø.

End [0]Ø racism now!
You never know when you might need [1]___ nurse. More pay for nurses!
Say NO to [2]___ terrorism!
There is an answer to war. [3]___ answer is peace.
[4]___ Amazon rainforest belongs to everyone.
Graffiti is [5]___ crime. Keep our city clean.
Save [6]___ planet.
[7]___ TOKYO WANTS THE OLYMPIC GAMES!

4 ★★★ Complete the telephone conversation with *a/an*, *the* or Ø.

A: Hi, Kevin.
B: Anna! It's you ... I mean, hi. It's good to hear from you.
A: Yeah? Are you sure?
B: Of course, sorry. I was busy with something …
A: I see. Well, how's life in [0]Ø London?
B: Oh pretty good, thanks. It's great studying in [1]___ capital city.
A: Are you enjoying the course?
B: Yes. There's a long way to go, but I'm still hoping to be [2]___ big, successful lawyer one day.
A: Ha! Well, I'm sure you'll be [3]___ best. You're very dedicated, after all.
B: Well, er … thanks. I've moved into [4]___ new flat, actually.
A: Oh cool. What's it like?
B: Well, [5]___ flat is quite small, but I've got my own.
A: Great! Does that mean I can come and visit?
B: Er … well … there's a bit of [6]___ problem, actually. I've kind of met someone and I'm not sure she'd understand if you …
A: But Kevin, we broke up. We're not boyfriend and girlfriend anymore, right?
B: Right, right. I know, but …
A: So we can't even be [7]___ friends now?
B: Well, we can, but I … well, it's difficult, Anna. I don't know what to say.
A: Well, thanks very much, Kevin.
B: Anna, I'm sorry … Anna? Anna, are you there?

SHOW WHAT YOU'VE LEARNT

5 Find and correct the mistakes in the sentences.

0 We try to provide ~~a food and water~~ for the poorest families. *Ø food and water*
1 For me, Paris is a very special city. It's a city where I was born. ______
2 I'd like to become the journalist and report on our country's problems. ______
3 An economic development is positive, but not if it destroys the environment. ______
4 Pencils will not be allowed in the exam. Please bring the pen. ______
5 Hill that overlooks Barcelona is the best place to view the city. ______
6 Is this an only place to eat around here? ______

/6

5.3 Listening language practice

An eco-school • Collocations • Compound nouns

1 Read the extract from an interview with a student about a project for an eco-school. Choose the correct options to complete the collocations in bold. Then listen and check.

Extract from Students' Book recording CD•2.37 MP3•80

A: First of all, we have solar panels on the roof of the school. [...]

B: And will they [1]*use / provide / have* **power** for the whole school?

A: Yes, that's the idea. It will [2]*pay / cost / save* **a lot of money on electricity**. [...]
Our eco-school will [3]*eat / grow / cook* **vegetables** and we'll use them for school dinners. [...] We'll also have chickens, rabbits and ducks.

B: And will they go into the school dinners too?

A: Ha, ha, no! That would be terrible. They'll be pets and they'll be useful. They'll [4]*throw away / use / eat* **the leftovers** from the kitchen and the chickens will [5]*provide / eat / collect* **eggs**.

B: Very good. So what other plans do you have to make the school more environmentally friendly?

A: We'll [6]*use / buy / make* **low-energy light bulbs** in all the classrooms. We'll also [7]*clean / have / empty* **recycling bins** in every classroom and in the school grounds.

B: And what about your lessons – will they be different from non-eco-schools?

A: Most of our lessons will be similar to lessons in any secondary school. But in our Science lessons we'll [8]*focus / think / learn* more **on environmental issues** like climate change and global warming. Then, in our Technology lessons we'll [9]*consider / learn / study* **about things like** renewable energy and even how to make solar panels.

B: I see. Well, we've almost run out of time. Thank you for talking to us about your project. It's very nice to meet a teenager who is so [10]*confused / concerned / nervous* **about the environment**. [...]

REMEMBER THIS

When completing collocations in exam tasks, look out for prepositions that can give you clues to the correct answers. Ask yourself which verbs go with which prepositions.

consider ~~about~~ things ✗ *study ~~about~~ things* ✗
learn about things ✓

2 Complete the sentences with collocations from Exercise 1. Change the verb forms if necessary.

0 If you turn down the heating at home, you'll use less energy and *save a lot of money on electricity*.
1 If Peter can't finish all the food on his plate, his dad always ____________ .
2 The wind farm currently ____________ for local houses.
3 The school now ____________ outside the main building, so please separate your rubbish.
4 If you are really ____________ , why don't you sell that big car and buy something greener?
5 To save energy, the council will make sure all the street lights in the city ____________ .
6 Jeremy and Pat ____________ , herbs and fruit in their garden.
7 Vote for the Green Party. We promise to ____________ , not on defence and industry.
8 At the moment in Maths, we ____________ Algebra.
9 A local farm ____________ all the eggs used in this restaurant.

WORD STORE 5E

Compound nouns – the environment

3 Choose the correct answer, A, B or C.

1 There are recycling ___ in our apartment block, but some people still don't separate plastic and paper.
A bins B panels C issues
2 Despite all the evidence, there are still people who don't believe that climate ___ is real.
A warming B recycling C change
3 This backpack has small solar ___ on it and you can actually use it to charge your phone.
A panels B climates C light bulbs
4 Global ___ is causing the ice caps in both the Arctic and the Antarctic to melt.
A environment B warming C change
5 Renewable ___ is the future. We can't continue burning fossil fuels forever.
A energy B recycling C low-energy
6 The developing world is facing serious ___ issues such as air pollution and water contamination.
A climate B change C environmental
7 The Energy Minister is in trouble after newspapers reported that she does not use low-energy ___ in her own home.
A bins B light bulbs C panels

5.4 Reading

A very bright idea • Adjective-noun collocations

Glossary

attempt (n, v) = try
angle (n,v) = the space between two straight lines that join each other; you measure it in degrees, e.g. 30, 45, 90
ray (n) = a straight, narrow line of light, e.g. from the sun, the moon or a laser
shade (n) = slight darkness or protection from the sun made by something blocking it, e.g. an umbrella
top up (v) = to increase the level of something and make it full again, e.g. your mobile phone credit
residents (n) = the people who live in a particular place or building

A very bright idea

The sun makes life on Earth possible. Almost all plants and animals rely on its warmth and heat to stay alive. For us humans, it also provides many simple pleasures such as long summer evenings, bright winter days and the feeling of warm sunlight on our faces. Imagine the frustration of living somewhere where, even when the sun is shining, people can't feel its heat or appreciate its light. [1]___

For six months of the year, Rjukan, a town of 3,500 people located 100 miles west of Oslo, is cut off from direct sunlight by the steep forested hills that surround it. [2]___ Of course, many Scandinavian towns and cities suffer from freezing cold temperatures in the winter months, but Rjukan's residents have had to cope with a complete lack of sunlight as well. In an early attempt to find a solution to this problem, a cable car was built in 1928, which allowed the town's citizens to ride to the top of the hill and top up their vitamin D.

These days however, the people of Rjukan can stand in their central square and enjoy the warmth and the light of the winter sun. How is this possible? What has changed? Well, the answer might seem like something from a science-fiction story, but in fact, it is reality. Authorities have placed three giant mirrors on top of the hills surrounding the town to reflect light down into the valley. [3]___ As a result of this investment and of the unusual flights, the town now benefits from a 600-square-metre area of light which brightens the central square. 'We think it will mean more activities in town, especially in autumn and wintertime,' said Karin Roe, head of the town's tourist office. 'People will be out more.'

The mirrors are controlled by a computer to follow the sun and adjust to the best angle to catch the rays and reflect them onto the centre of the town. [4]___ However, it was only made possible with modern technology. Solar panels power equipment to automatically wash the mirrors and move them into position.

Steinar Bergsland, the town's mayor, said, 'It is really special to stand in the light down on the square and feel the heat. This is for the pale little children of Rjukan.' A message on the Rjukan tourist website states, 'The square will become a sunny meeting place in a town which is otherwise in the shade.'

[5]___ A similar project was completed in Italy in 2006, when the residents of Viganella installed mirrors on the hills above their village to take advantage of the sunlight that shone there.

1 Read the article quickly and choose the newspaper section that you think it would *not* appear in.

1 Environment news ☐
2 Technology news ☐
3 Tourism news ☐
4 Winter sports news ☐
5 Scandinavian news ☐

2 Read the article again and choose from the sentences (A–F) the one which fits each gap (1–5). There is one extra sentence.

A The huge mirrors were carried there by helicopters, as part of a project which cost 5 million kroner (£500,000). ☐
B This happens because between September and March, the sun is so low in the sky that its light and warmth don't reach the small town in the bottom of the valley. ☐
C Environmentalists disapprove of the project, however. ☐
D The town of Rjukan, in Norway, is just such a place. ☐
E In fact, Rjukan is not the only place to benefit from this kind of scheme. ☐
F The idea was first suggested 100 years ago by Sam Eyde, who was responsible for building the town of Rjukan. ☐

3 Read the article again. Are the statements true (T) or false (F)?

1 Many Scandinavian towns suffer from a complete lack of sunlight. ☐
2 The mirrors project is not the first attempt to solve the problem in Rjukan. ☐
3 The idea for the mirrors project came from a science fiction story. ☐
4 Mirrors have been placed in the town square to reflect the sunlighs. ☐
5 The movement of the mirrors is powered by the sun. ☐
6 This is the first time anyone has successfully completed such a project. ☐

4 Match 1–5 with a–e to make extracts from the article.

0 … many Scandinavian towns **suffer** [f]
1 The mirrors (…) **adjust** ☐
2 They installed mirrors (…) to **take advantage** ☐
3 … the town now **benefits** ☐
4 Sam Eyde (…) was **responsible** ☐
5 … residents had to **cope** ☐

a **of** the sunlight that shone there.
b **from** a 600-square-metre area of light …
c **with** a complete lack of sunlight …
d **for** building the town of Rjukan.
e **to** the best angle to catch the rays …
f **from** freezing cold temperatures in the winter …

5 Complete the sentences with the words in bold in Exercise 4. Change the verb forms if necessary.

0 The air pollution in this city means that many residents *suffer from* serious allergies.
1 People in this region have learned to _______ the destructive effects of tropical storms.
2 Every person on the planet is _______ reducing global warming. We all need to change our behaviour.
3 It may take some time to _______ life in the countryside after living in the city for so many years.
4 We invite hotel guests to _______ our free airport bus service.
5 The only people who _______ illegal logging are the loggers themselves.

REMEMBER BETTER

After some verbs and adjectives, we put a particular preposition before the object. Make two-sided memory cards to help you remember the correct combinations. Start by making cards like the one below for the combinations in Exercise 4. You can use this technique to learn new verbs and adjectives with prepositions found in a dictionary or online.

My sister always **suffers** _______ colds in winter.	**from**

WORD STORE 5F
Adjective-noun collocations

6 Complete the text with the words in the box. There are two extra words.

endangered environmental ~~dense~~ global interactive local outside renewable

Survival – the global movement for tribal people's rights

Survival

Imagine what it would be like to be a member of a tribe that lives in the middle of a [0] *dense* rainforest.

Research suggests that in countries such as Brazil, there are still some forest tribes that have little or no idea that the [1] _______ community exists at all. It is likely that the members of these tribes have never left their [2] _______ communities and know nothing of the [3] _______ world. However, they almost certainly know every square-metre of the forests around the area in which they live. They don't need [4] _______ maps or GPS to find their way around. As more and more forests are cut down, it is not only [5] _______ species of plants and animals that we need to be concerned about, but also the people who call the forest their home. If you would like to know more, visit www.survivalinternational.org.

5.5 Grammar

Non-defining relative clauses

SHOW WHAT YOU KNOW

1 Complete the sentences with the words in the box and relative pronouns. There are two extra words.

bangle ~~coast~~ court embassy
opponent ostrich pitch tour leader

0 The *coast* is a place *where* the sea meets the land.
1 A(n) _____ is a large flightless bird _____ lives in Africa.
2 A(n) _____ is a person _____ travels with and looks after a group of tourists.
3 A(n) _____ is a place _____ cricket, football, rugby and hockey are played.
4 A(n) _____ is jewellery _____ is worn round the wrist.
5 A(n) _____ is a place _____ an ambassador works.

2 ★ Read the text and choose the correct options.

sparebrain – your online encyclopedia

Tōhoku earthquake and tsunami

The 2011 tsunami in Japan, [1]*which / that* hit the Tōhoku region on Pacific coast, was caused by a huge undersea earthquake. The earthquake, [2]*what / which* was the most powerful ever to hit Japan, created waves of up to 40.5 metres high and killed over 15,000 people. In Sendai, [3]*which / where* is the largest city in the region, the waves travelled up to 10km inland. In Fukushima, [4]*where / whose* Fukushima Daiichi Nuclear Power Plant is located, there was a major nuclear disaster. Naoto Kan, [5]*who / whose* was the Prime Minister at the time, said, 'In the sixty-five years after World War II, this is the toughest crisis for Japan.' The World Bank, [6]*who / whose* goal is to increase development and reduce global poverty, said that cleaning up and rebuilding after the tsunami would cost more than after any other natural disaster in world history.

3 ★★ Write sentences with non-defining relative clauses. Use the correct form of *be*.

0 Australia / sixth largest country in the world / home to a relatively small population
Australia, which is the sixth largest country in the world, is home to a relatively small population.
1 Sydney / the famous opera house can be found / not actually the capital of Australia
____
2 Australian actress Nicole Kidman / films include *Moulin Rouge* and *The Others* / actually born in Hawaii
____
3 Hugh Jackman / known for playing Wolverine in the *X-Men* films / from Sydney
____
4 in South Australia, Anna Creek Cattle Station / over 34,000km^2 / larger than Belgium
____

4 ★★★ Complete the text with relative pronouns. Add commas where necessary.

sparebrain – your online encyclopedia

Charles Darwin

Charles Darwin.

Charles Darwin, [0]*who* was born on 11 February 1809, was an English naturalist and geologist. He was the first person to suggest that all species evolved from a single form of life. He also suggested the theory of natural selection [1]_____ attempts to explain why there are now so many different forms of life on Earth.

In the Galapagos Islands [2]_____ Darwin studied local birds he found strong evidence to support his theories. Natural selection [3]_____ is sometimes called 'survival of the fittest' is still the most popular scientific explanation for the variety of life found on our planet. Darwin [4]_____ ideas were questioned at first is now famous as one of the most important thinkers in human history.

SHOW WHAT YOU'VE LEARNT

5 Rewrite the sentences using relative clauses for the information in brackets.

0 Mount Vesuvius, *(it last erupted in 1944)*, is a popular tourist attraction today.
Mount Vesuvius, which last erupted in 1944, is a popular tourist attraction today.
1 My cousin, *(he lives in Manhattan)*, has an apartment overlooking the city.
My cousin, _____________________________________, has an apartment overlooking the city.
2 Our new car, *(we bought it this year)*, is environmentally friendly.
Our new car, _____________________________________, is environmentally friendly.
3 Poland, *(it's in central Europe)*, has a very diverse climate.
Poland, _____________________________________, has a very diverse climate.
4 Northern Ireland, *(it's the smallest country in the UK)*, has a population of around 2 million.
Northern Ireland, _____________________________________, has a population of around 2 million.
5 These low-energy light bulbs, *(they are supposed to save money)*, are actually quite expensive.
These low-energy light bulbs, _____________________________________, are actually quite expensive.

/5

5.6 Speaking language practice

Expressing and justifying an opinion

1 Label the phrases *D* for discussing different options or *C* for choosing one of the options and justifying the choice.

0 What about this idea? [D]
1 I wouldn't choose the picture showing … because … [ ]
2 I'm not so sure. [ ]
3 I'd go for picture X because … [ ]
4 Let's start with this one. [ ]
5 I completely agree with you. [ ]
6 Out of these three pictures, I'd choose picture X because … [ ]

2 Read the discussion task and then complete the conversation two students had about it. The first letter of each word is given.

Here are some things we can do to help the environment.

1 Talk to each other about how useful these things are for helping the environment.
2 Decide which of these things can help most.

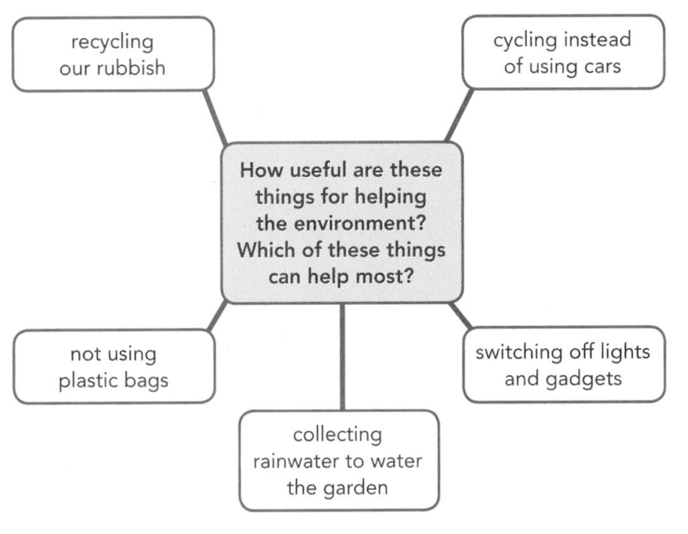

recycling our rubbish
cycling instead of using cars
How useful are these things for helping the environment? Which of these things can help most?
not using plastic bags
switching off lights and gadgets
collecting rainwater to water the garden

A: OK. [1]**L**_____ **s**_____ **w**_____ **t**_____ **o**_____ – recycling our rubbish. I think this is really useful because then we don't throw so much onto landfill sites. [2]**W**_____ **d**_____ **y**_____ **t**_____?
B: Yes, [3]**y**_____ **r**_____. It helps the countryside and we can also make new products from the rubbish that we recycle. [4]**W**_____ **a**_____ **t**_____ **i**_____ – cycling instead of using cars?
A: I [5]**t**_____ **t**_____ **i**_____ a **g**_____ **i**_____. It's also very healthy for people to do.
B: I [6]**c**_____ **a**_____ **w**_____ **y**_____. It makes the air much better and we don't use so much petrol.
A: Switching off lights and gadgets. Do you think that's useful?
B: [7]**I**_____ **n**_____ **s**_____ **s**_____. I don't think it saves much energy, do you?
A: No, but not using plastic bags is good. They can cause a lot of damage to animals, especially birds.
B: And they last for hundreds of years! We don't collect rainwater; do you?

Let's keep our world clean together!!! Please recycle rubbish.
Please recycle your rubbish.
Slam-dunk your junk!
Recycle your rubbish and live a little greener.

A: [8]**T**_____ **p**_____ **w**_____ **t**_____ **i**_____ you need a big thing to collect it and some people don't have anywhere to put it!
B: True!
A: So, which of these things can help most? [9]**P**_____, I **w**_____ **g**_____ **f**_____ switching off lights.
B: You're right. [10]**O**_____ **o**_____ **t**_____ **i**_____, **I**_____ **g**_____ **f**_____ the recycling. Everyone can do it and it's really useful.
A: I completely agree with you.

3 Rewrite the sentences. Use the words in brackets.

0 The three photographs show different environments.
The three photographs *focus on different environments*. (focus)

1 I wouldn't choose poster 2 because it's too shocking.
______________________________ because it's too shocking. (reason)

2 Picture 2 isn't as funny as picture 3.
______________________________ (funnier)

3 I think the best option would be picture 2 because it's clear and simple.
______________________________ because it's clear and simple. (choose)

4 I don't like picture 3 because it's too old-fashioned.
______________________________ because it's old-fashioned. (go for)

5 Poster 3 is more interesting than the other posters.
______________________________ (not as … as)

6 The message in poster 2 is not clear.
______________________________ the message is not clear. (problem)

5.7 Writing

A 'for and against' essay

1 Read the first paragraph of the essay and decide which statement is being discussed. Don't worry about the words in italics for now.

1 It would be better if everyone in the world spoke the same language. ☐
2 Everyone in the world should learn to speak at least one foreign language. ☐
3 All the world's school pupils should study the Mandarin language. ☐

Experts say there are nearly 7,000 languages in the world today. Huge amounts of money and time are spent on learning and translating languages. It is not surprising that some people believe life would be simpler if we all spoke the same language. [1]*For example / However*, other people feel that language is an essential part of identity, and that a global language would not make the world a simpler place.

[2]*On the one hand / On the other hand*, there are arguments for the idea of a single language. [3]*Secondly / Firstly*, for business people, the language barrier would no longer be a problem. [4]*For instance / To sum up*, international companies would not have to spend large sums of money on translation. [5]*Secondly / Thirdly*, a single world language would probably be good for tourism. [6]*For example / Finally*, tourists would feel safer visiting certain countries if they knew they could communicate easily.

[7]*On the one hand / On the other hand*, there are important arguments against a single global language. [8]*First of all / However*, a nation's language is a significant part of its culture and character. For example, when Poland was occupied by other countries in the past, the Polish language helped people to keep their identity as Poles. [9]*For instance / Furthermore*, many people get pleasure, satisfaction and income from studying, using and teaching languages. For such people, a single global language would not be an advantage.

[10]*In conclusion / Finally*, although there are some reasonable arguments for the idea of a single world language, it is hard to imagine it could ever happen. [11]*Finally / In my opinion*, if there ever was a single language, the world would be a far less interesting place.

2 Read the essay and choose the correct options.

język JEZIK Sprache language lingvo jazyk lengua lingua språk sprog langue

3 Complete the table about linkers with the words in the box.

finally | for instance | give a personal opinion | give examples | introduce a conclusion | ~~list arguments~~ | personally, I think | show contrast

Use	Examples
[0] *list arguments*	First of all/Firstly/Secondly/ [1] ______
[2] ______	For example/[3] ______
[4] ______	However/On the one hand/ On the other hand
[5] ______	In my opinion/[6] ______
[7] ______	In conclusion/In summary

4 You are going to write a 'for and against' essay discussing the question *Can money buy you happiness?* Mark these arguments for (F) or against (A).

1 People get pleasure from nice possessions. ☐
2 Friendship and love don't cost anything. ☐
3 In many places education and healthcare is not free. ☐
4 If you have money you can see the world. ☐
5 Life is full of simple pleasures. ☐
6 Happiness comes from achieving your goals. ☐

SHOW WHAT YOU'VE LEARNT

5 In your English class you have been talking about money and happiness. Now your teacher has asked you to write an essay. Write your essay using all the notes and give reasons for your point of view.

Can money buy you happiness?
Notes
- friendship
- health
- ______ (your own idea)

Write your essay in 140–190 words.

SHOW THAT YOU'VE CHECKED

In my 'for and against' essay:

- I have started the first paragraph with general or factual comments about the topic. ☐
- I have ended the first paragraph with a statement mentioning both sides of the topic. ☐
- I have presented arguments for and against the topic and supported them with examples in the other paragraphs. ☐
- I have included a summarising statement and my personal opinion in the final paragraph. ☐
- I have checked my spelling and punctuation. ☐
- I have written at least 140 words. ☐

5.8 Use of English

Multiple-choice cloze

1 **For questions 1–9, read the article below and decide which answer (A, B, C or D) best fits each gap. There is an example at the beginning.**

Can wolves change rivers?

It doesn't seem very likely, does it? How can [0]___ species of wild dog change the course of a river? Let's find out.

In Yellowstone National Park, [1]___ is thought to be the oldest national park in the world, by the 1990s the wolf had been [2]___ for over seventy years. Then, in 1995, wolves were reintroduced. By then, the [3]___ of deer and other large plant-eating animals had risen greatly [4]___ there were no predators left to hunt them. Wolves, of course, [5]___ meat, including deer, so when wolves came, back deer numbers went down. As deer numbers went down, more plants and trees grew in the forests. These helped to stop the river [6]___ from collapsing into the river, so in time the rivers in Yellowstone became straighter. So yes, wolves can actually change rivers!

It doesn't stop there, either. Straighter rivers support more life, so there were more fish and plants in the rivers. Other [7]___ of the forest began to appear in greater numbers as the environment changed. The numbers of small birds, mice and rabbits went up first. Eagles eat small birds, mice and rabbits, so then more eagles appeared. Bears eat fruit, berries, small mammals and fish, so their numbers [8]___ too. Scientists say Yellowstone Park should make a complete [9]___ , all thanks in great part to one of its lost animals: the wolf.

	A	B	C	D
0	an	that	the	(D) a
1	where	that	which	what
2	dead	killed	finished	extinct
3	population	total	measure	size
4	however	because	although	so
5	kill	feed	eat	hunt
6	banks	sides	edges	borders
7	people	lives	inhabitants	citizens
8	expanded	lifted	raised	increased
9	recreation	recovery	relief	response

TIPS:

Question 1: You need a relative pronoun, but be careful! Is the relative clause about a place or thing?
Question 2: Which word is used when a type of animal disappears completely?
Question 3: Think of a word that is used to describe large numbers of animals or people.

Word formation

2 **For questions 1–8, read the article below. Use the word given in capitals at the end of some of the lines to form a word that fits in the gap in the same line. There is an example at the beginning.**

My report about sharks

If you mention sharks, most people think of a [0]*frightening* monster. But recently, more and more	FRIGHT
[1]___________ are trying to change public opinion about these animals. Many shark species are	SCIENCE
becoming [2]___________ because every year, an estimated 100 million sharks are killed by humans.	DANGER
The main reason for this [3]___________ is soup. It may seem very hard to believe but the huge	DESTROY
[4]___________ market for shark fin soup has created this problem. There are enormous	GLOBE
[5]___________ benefits for fishermen to change their normal fishing habits and catch sharks instead.	ECONOMY
Many of them live in [6]___________ and selling sharks' fins offers a higher income.	POOR
We need to raise [7]___________ of this issue with the consumers of shark fin soup. Sharks are not a	AWARE
[8]___________ source. Once they are gone, they are gone forever.	NEW

TIPS:

Question 1: What do we call the people who study or work in this subject?
Question 2: You need to add a suffix and also to make one other change to the word.
Question 3: You need to form a noun here.

5.9 Self-assessment

1 For each learning objective, tick the box that best matches your ability.

☺☺ = I understand and can help a friend.
☺ = I understand and can do it by myself.
☹ = I understand some, but have some questions.
☹☹ = I do not understand.

			☺☺	☺	☹	☹☹	Need help?
5.1	Vocabulary	I can talk about geography and natural disasters.					Students' Book pages 60–61 Word Store page 11 Workbook pages 56–57
5.2	Grammar	I can use articles correctly.					Students' Book page 62 Workbook page 58
5.3	Listening	I can identify specific detail in an interview.					Students' Book page 63 Workbook page 59
5.4	Reading	I can understand the structure of a text.					Students' Book pages 64–65 Workbook pages 60–61
5.5	Grammar	I can use non-defining relative clauses.					Students' Book page 66 Workbook page 62
5.6	Speaking	I can express and justify an opinion.					Students' Book page 67 Workbook page 63
5.7	Writing	I can present and support arguments in a 'for and against' essay.					Students' Book pages 68–69 Workbook page 64

2 What can you remember from this unit?

New words I learned (the words you most want to remember from this unit)	**Expressions and phrases I liked** (any expressions or phrases you think sound nice, useful or funny)	**English I heard or read outside class** (e.g. from websites, books, adverts, films, music)

5.10 Self-check

1 Complete the words in the sentences. Some letters are given.

0 The best place to eat seafood is in one of the restaurants on the **c**oas**t** overlooking the sea.
1 The water in the **b**______**y** is much calmer than the water in the open sea.
2 With the hills on either side of you, follow the river along the bottom of the **v**______**y** until you reach the village.
3 Before you can begin climbing the high mountains, you have to cross the lower **f**______**s** on horseback.
4 The **c**______**e** in Thailand is tropical, which means it is hot and humid for most of the year.
5 Residents are being evacuated before the **h**______**e** hits the area tomorrow. Winds of up to 120km per hour are expected.

/5

2 Match the sentence halves. Then complete the missing words. The last two letters of each word are given.

0 Some scientists say renewable [e]
1 Since we started using low-energy [ ]
2 Here on the top there are solar [ ]
3 Six people are missing in the dense [ ]
4 Numbers of this previously endangered [ ]
5 Members of the local [ ]

a _____**ls** which provide power for the lights.
b _____**es** of frog are slowly increasing again.
c _____**ty** support the development plans.
d _____**ht** _____**bs**, we've saved a lot of money.
e ener**gy** is the best alternative to nuclear power.
f _____**st** to the north of the village.

/5

3 Complete the sentences with the correct form of the verbs in the box. There are two extra verbs.

destroy burst erupt flood
flow locate ~~overlook~~ strike

0 I booked a room with a sea view, but my room overlooks the car park.
1 This river __________ from here to the Pacific Ocean, which is over 1,000km away.
2 A volcano __________ in Chile yesterday and sent smoke and ash over 2km up into the sky.
3 In February 2011 an earthquake __________ Christchurch, New Zealand and killed 185 people.
4 Police are trying to __________ the missing man, who was last seen on Thursday night.
5 Over 10,000 books were __________ when a library caught fire in the city centre last night.

/5

4 Complete the sentences with *a/an, the* or Ø (no article).

0 Ladies and gentlemen, we have landed in Ø Madrid.
1 Last night I had ___ strange dream. The dream was about my teacher.
2 When Clara leaves school, she wants to be ___ architect.
3 Kevin has a plan. Actually, ___ plan was Ian's idea, but Kevin told us about it.
4 ___ swimming pool at our school is very old and a bit scary.
5 ___ unemployment in the country has fallen recently.

/5

5 Add *who, which, where* or *whose* and commas to form sentences with non-defining relative clauses.

0 Katie, who lives next door, looks after lost and injured animals.
1 Stratford-upon-Avon I was brought up is famous as the birthplace of William Shakespeare.
2 Singapore is an island country in South-East Asia is an extremely clean and tidy place.
3 Prince George of Cambridge great grandmother is the Queen of England was born in 2013.
4 Ganesha is a Hindu god has an elephant's head.
5 Penang is an island off the coast of Malaysia is sometimes called 'the Pearl of the Orient'.

/5

6 Read the text and choose the correct answer, A, B or C.

Focus on: North Korea

[0]___ North Korea, [1]___ is officially known as the Democratic People's Republic of Korea, is an unusual and secretive socialist country. The ordinary people of North Korea rarely have any contact with the [2]___ world because it is impossible for them to travel overseas or access the Internet. The rest of the world knows very little about what life is like in North Korea because it is not part of the wider [3]___ community. Kim Jong-un, [4]___ is currently the supreme leader of North Korea is the third member of the Kim family to lead the Republic since it was established in 1948. [5]___ capital city is called Pyongyang and is located in the south-west of the country.

	A	B	C
0	(A Ø)	The	A
1	where	which	who
2	inside	outside	other
3	global	local	national
4	which	whose	who
5	Ø	The	A

/5

Total /30

6 GET WELL

6.1 Vocabulary

Parts of the body • Injuries • Body idioms

SHOW WHAT YOU KNOW

1 Label the parts of the body. The first letter of each word is given.

2 Complete the sentences with words for parts of the body.

0 I've painted my *fingernails* the same colour as my new dress.
1 In many European countries, male friends kiss female friends on the __________ but not usually on the lips.
2 Granddad bit into a nut and broke his left front __________ .
3 Some geckos, a type of lizard, lick their own eyes clean with their __________ .
4 When you are trying on ski boots, make sure your __________ stay on the bottom of the boot and don't lift up when you lean forward.
5 Although it's rare, some people are born with six fingers on one hand or six __________ on one foot. The condition is called polydactylism.
6 We sell shoes in very large sizes for people with unusually big __________ .

WORD STORE 6A
Parts of the body

3 Read the adverts and choose the correct options.

Aching muscles in your [1]*thumbs / thighs* and your [2]*calves / elbows*? Relaxing leg massages only €10 for 30 minutes.

Do your [3]*eyebrows / lips* look like hairy caterpillars? Let Beverly the Beautician restore your beauty.

Click the blue [5]*toe / thumb* to like us on Facebook.

[4]*Lips / Knees* not kissable enough? You need our deep protecting balm.

Attention all boxers! Our new mouth-guards protect your teeth and your [6]*jaws / hands* in the ring.

Our new hiking boots support your [7]*thighs / ankles* and reduce the pain in your [8]*chest / knees* caused by long days walking in the mountains.

WORD STORE 6B
Word families – injuries

4 Complete the conversations with the correct form of the words in brackets.

Conversation 1: Mum and Gavin

G: Mum, I'm calling from the hospital. It's about Ollie. He's got a [0]*sprained* (sprain) ankle.
M: What! Oh Gavin, your little brother! You were supposed to look after him. What happened? Are you sure it's not [1]______ (break)?
G: Mum, it's not my fault! He [2]______ (sprain) it skateboarding. Anyway, I drove us here and he's OK. The doctor says it's not a serious [3]______ (sprain).
M: He's OK? Gavin! Why didn't you call me immediately? Is he upset?
G: It's OK, Mum! He's fine. He's [4]______ (scratch) his knee and he's got a [5]______ (cut) on his forehead.
M: He's [6]______ (cut) his forehead! Oh my beautiful boy!
G: Ha, ha! Don't let him hear you say that.
M: Gavin! This is not funny.
G: Mum, chill out! It's not like he's got a horrible [7]______ (burn) or anything. He'll be fine. Actually, he thinks it's cool. He says he hopes he has a scar and the doctor called him a tough guy.
M: Cool? A scar? Did he bang his head and go crazy? I'm on my way!

Conversation 2: Doctor and Agata

D: Do you want the good news or the bad news, Agata?

A: Good news? Is there any good news?

D: Well, yes. You have a [8]_____ (bruise) elbow and you've [9]_____ (dislocate) your shoulder, but you haven't [10]_____ (break) it.

A: OK … and that is good, is it?

D: Well, a [11]_____ (dislocate) shoulder is not usually as painful as a [12]_____ (break) shoulder and in your case, it's going to be a lot easier to fix.

A: Will I be able to ski again this week? We only arrived yesterday.

D: Er, that's the bad news, I'm afraid. After a [13]_____ (dislocate) like this, we recommend that you rest completely for at least six weeks.

A: Six weeks? Are you joking?

REMEMBER BETTER

To help you remember the vocabulary in this section, make a list of injuries you or people you know have had.

Joe dislocated his toe when he was playing football.
I've never broken a bone.
I've got a scratch on my hand now (from our cat).

WORD STORE 6C
Body idioms

5 Complete the sentences with the words in the box. There are two extra words.

bottom eyes ~~hand~~ head
heart leg thumb tongue

0 I've sprained my wrist and I can't lift anything heavy. Could you give me a *hand* with my luggage?
1 When she showed us the bruise, we couldn't believe our ________ . It covers the whole of her thigh!
2 When Frieda's cat died, it broke her ________ . I told her it was just a cat and she slammed the door in my face.
3 What's it called again? You know … er … thingy. Oh come on! It's on the tip of my ________ .
4 It's your birthday? Really? But I didn't get you anything. Or did I? Ha, ha! I'm only pulling your ________ . Here's your gift. Happy birthday!
5 When I saw Jason dressed as nurse Florence Nightingale, I laughed my ________ off.

REMEMBER THIS

Take care not to overuse idioms. Most idioms are only used occasionally by native speakers. Consider how often you use them in your own language and use this as a guide.

6 Complete idioms 1–6 with the correct verbs. Then match them with definitions a–f.

1 __________ someone a hand
2 __________ on the tip of your tongue
3 __________ someone's leg
4 __________ head off
5 __________ someone's heart
6 __________ your eyes

a be very surprised
b laugh a lot
c joke with someone
d upset someone very much
e almost remember a word
f help someone

SHOW WHAT YOU'VE LEARNT

7 Choose the correct answer, A, B or C, to complete both sentences in each pair.

1 I hope I never ___ a bone. It must be so painful.
I'm exhausted. Can we take a ___ for half an hour?
A rest B hurt C break
2 Your socks are right at the ___ of the bag. Take everything out and you'll find them.
A bruised ___ is very common for snowboarders. That's the body part you usually land on when you fall.
A bottom B top C arm
3 I'm afraid it'll take long to see a doctor. Please be ___ .
My daughter is a ___ in this hospital. When can I visit her?
A patient B burn C calm
4 It was so funny when he fell over. I laughed my ___ off.
Behave yourself or I'll send you to the ___ teacher.
A eyes B mouth C head
5 Lucy has a ___ on her foot. She stepped on some broken glass.
___ the chicken into six pieces and cover with olive oil and a little salt and pepper.
A scratch B cut C chop

8 Choose the correct options.

1 Jack has a *burnt / sprained / dislocated* thumb. He didn't put the glove on when he took the pizza out of the oven.
2 Look at the size of the muscles in her *heels / ankles / calves*. She must be a marathon runner.
3 What is the actress in *The Hunger Games* called? It's on the tip of my *teeth / tongue / lips*. Jennifer something.
4 When I saw the comedian on television last night, I laughed my *face / mouth / head* off!
5 Most people have two *ankles / thumbs / eyebrows*, but Ryan's meet in the middle, so it looks like he has just one.

/10

6.2 Grammar

Second Conditional • *wish/if only*

SHOW WHAT YOU KNOW

1 Read the sentences and choose the correct meaning, A or B.

1 If I had a pair of winter boots, my feet wouldn't be cold.
A The speaker's feet are cold.
B The speaker's feet aren't cold.

2 My brother and I wouldn't fall out if he wasn't so immature.
A The speaker's brother is immature.
B The speaker's brother is not immature.

3 She'd need glasses if she was short-sighted.
A She needs glasses. B She doesn't need glasses.

4 Peter, you'd find writing more difficult if you were left-handed.
A Peter is right-handed. B Peter is left-handed.

5 Polly wouldn't hang out with Ella if they didn't have so much in common.
A Polly and Ella are very different.
B Polly and Ella are very similar.

2 ★ Read the article and choose the correct options.

RANDOMQUESTIONS

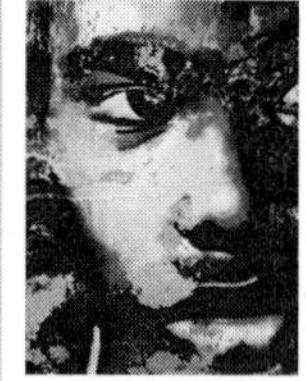

Today's online guest is British teenage rap sensation

Mikey Silence

Latest questions (there are 171 people logged in)

20.08 **Clairewiththehair**

What would you do if you weren't a rapper?

Hi, Claire. Interesting name. I [1]*wouldn't be / 'd be* a doctor or a teacher if I [2]*wasn't / wouldn't be* a rapper. I'd like to do something to help other people.

20.07 **Sk8r_132**

If you [3]*would have / had* a superpower, what would it be?

Interesting question, Sk8r. I'd love to be able to fly. If I [4]*would want / wanted* to get away from people for a while and be on my own or write some new lyrics. I [5]*'d fly / will fly* up to the clouds and just hang out there for a while. That would be pretty awesome.

20.05 **Lilliy422**

Which part of your body would you like to change?

Woah! Lilly, that's a bit of a personal question, I'm pretty happy as I am, to be honest. Nobody's perfect, but I don't really care what anybody else thinks. I suppose if I [6]*'d change / changed* anything I [7]*'d make / made* myself a bit taller. I love hanging out and playing basketball, but I am kind of short. ☹

waiting for next question …

3 ★★ Write Second Conditional sentences using the sentences in bold and the words in brackets. Use commas where necessary.

0 **I wish I didn't have this virus.** (I / go out / and meet my friends)
I'*d go out and meet my friends if I didn't have this virus*.

1 **If only the exam was next week.** (we / have / a bit longer for revision)
If ______________.

2 **I wish my legs were stronger.** (I / run / much further)
I ______________.

3 **If only we lived on the coast.** (I / walk / on the beach every day)
If ______________.

4 **I wish you liked fish.** (we / have / a healthier diet)
We ______________.

4 ★★★ Complete the second sentence to show that you would like the situation or behaviour to be different.

0 My brother borrows my clothes without asking.
I wish *my brother wouldn't borrow* my clothes without asking.

1 I have a dislocated finger.
If only ______________ a dislocated finger.

2 My boyfriend never calls me.
I wish ______________ call me.

3 Our school doesn't have recycling bins.
I wish ______________ recycling bins.

4 My girlfriend isn't talking to me.
If only ______________ to me.

5 Fast food is bad for you.
If only ______________ bad for you.

SHOW WHAT YOU'VE LEARNT

5 Find and correct the mistakes in the sentences.

0 If only driving lessons ~~would be~~ cheaper. *were*

1 If Lucas would have a suit, he'd wear it to the wedding. ______

2 We save a lot of money if we stayed over at Karen's house. ______

3 I wish I wouldn't be so pale-skinned. ______

4 I'd ate it if it wasn't so greasy. ______

5 If only broccoli tastes like chocolate. ______

6 I wish my shoes wouldn't smell so bad. ______

/6

6.3 Listening language practice

Prepositions • Verb patterns

1 Read the text and choose the correct answer, A, B or C. Then listen and check.

Students' Book recording CD•3.10 MP3•99

I'm sure everyone here knows all [1]______ the terrible illness, Ebola, which is affecting thousands and thousands of people in Africa. There have been a few cases in Europe and America, but the problem is still mainly in African countries. At the moment scientists are working very hard to find a vaccine because normal medicines don't work. People don't catch the illness [2]______ the air, but from touching other people who have it. This makes it hard [3]______ doctors and nurses who are looking [4]______ them. We really need to help them. They need more money [5]______ research, hospitals and more doctors. So that's why I'm talking to you today. The school is planning to have a walk for charity next weekend. Last year we organised a marathon swim and we raised over £3,000 for the local children's hospital. This time we hope to get more, perhaps over £5,000! The event will start [6]______ the school on Saturday morning at 10.30. The route will go [7]______ the forest and across the hills to Brockfield. The fastest walkers should take [8]______ three hours. The slowest, like me, will take quite a lot longer! But we hope the last people will arrive [9]______ Brockfield before 4.30. So get your trainers [10]______ and join us on Saturday to help fight Ebola!

	A	B	C
1	A on	B about	C for
2	A in	B out	C from
3	A for	B to	C at
4	A for	B on	C after
5	A to	B for	C of
6	A off	B on	C at
7	A in	B over	C through
8	A in	B for	C about
9	A by	B in	C up
10	A on	B down	C to

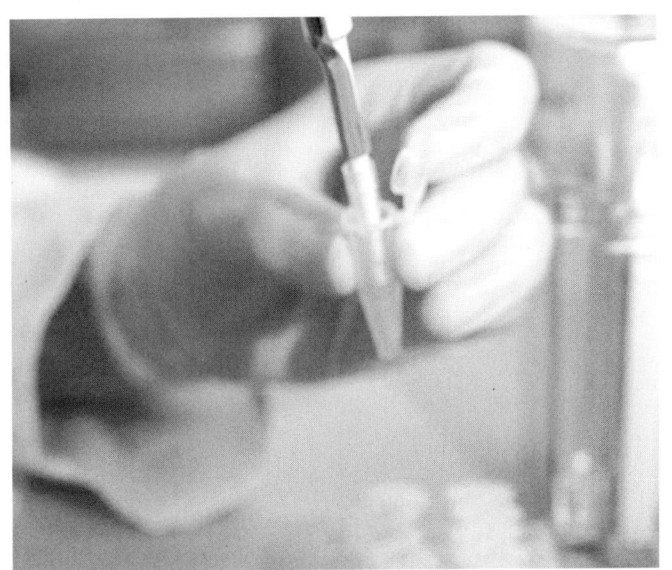

REMEMBER THIS

It is not easy to know which prepositions come after which verbs. Remember that different combinations are possible, depending on the context. For example, many verbs can be followed by either *for* + noun or a *to*-infinitive.

I want to ***raise*** *money* ***for charity****.*
I want to ***raise*** *money* ***to help*** *heart attack victims.*

2 Choose the correct options.

1 a I'm afraid you'll have to pay *to / for* see a private doctor.
  b Please pay *to / for* your popcorn before you start eating it!
2 a Visitors: queue here *to / for* the aquarium.
  b Do we queue here *to / for* buy a ticket for the match?
3 a Ronaldo has scored seventeen goals so far this season *to / for* his country.
  b England need to score one more goal *to / for* become world champions.
4 a Matthew is very serious about basketball. He always plays *to / for* win.
  b In my opinion, it's not right that foreign players play *to / for* the national team.
5 a Darling, I promise I'll always be there *to / for* you.
  b Don't worry about your sprained ankle. We'll be there *to / for* help you get up the stairs.

WORD STORE 6D

Compound nouns – health issues

3 Complete the words in the notice. The last letter of each word is given.

First Aid and Home Health Course for young people – starting next month

Would you know what to do if someone was having a [0]heart attack? Do you know how to stop a [1]______e bleed? If the answer is *no*, then maybe you should enrol on our First Aid and Home Health Course. We'll be learning practical things such as how to treat a [2]______k eye or deal with a [3]______e sting, as well as offering advice on things like preventing [4]______n burn and coping with [5]______y fever.

The course begins on 3 February and will be held every week for six weeks, between 16.00 and 17.30, in room 303. All students are welcome, but there are only twenty places, so be quick! For registration, see Mrs Barker in the school office.

Glossary

anaesthetist (n) = a medical professional who specialises in stopping patients from feeling pain during surgery
device (n) = a machine or tool that does a special job; a synonym for *gadget*
pancreatic (adj) = connected with the pancreas, an organ near the stomach that produces insulin

A lot of light bulbs

1 On first impressions, Jack Thomas Andraka is a pretty normal American teenager. A student of North County High School, near Baltimore, he was born in 1997 and raised in Maryland on the east coast of the US. His father is a civil engineer, his mother an anaesthetist and originally, his family comes from Poland. Jack is a keen scout who likes white water rafting and is a member of the National Junior Wildwater Kayak Team. He enjoys Maths at school, reading on his Kindle and watching crime series on TV.

2 Sounds pretty average, right? Well, in fact, this teenager is anything but average. Jack is the winner of several major science awards, the subject of a number of documentary films and a regular speaker at scientific and educational conferences around the world. Why? Because as well as being a regular teenage boy, he is also a world-famous inventor, pioneering cancer researcher and proof that you don't need a lifetime of experience to be able to invent something truly life-changing.

3 After the sad death of a friend from pancreatic cancer, the same illness that killed Apple founder Steve Jobs in 2011, Jack began doing research into the life-threatening condition. He discovered that one of the reasons so many people died from this particular type of cancer was because there was no cheap and reliable test that allowed doctors to diagnose the illness early enough to save the patient. Amazingly, Jack thought of a way to develop a simple test using things he had learned in his Biology class at school and through scientific journals and articles, some of which he found by chance online.

4 Jack needed money, assistance and a laboratory to continue developing his idea, so he contacted around 200 research professionals to ask for help. Unfortunately, 199 of the replies were negative, but the 200th from Dr Anirban Maitra, a professor at Johns Hopkins School of Medicine, was the one that Jack was waiting for. So, with the help of Professor Maitra and the use of his lab, Jack successfully developed a test for pancreatic cancer that is 168 times faster, 400 times more sensitive and 26,000 times less expensive than the current diagnostic tests. The test is even effective for two other types of cancer as well.

5 In 2012 Jack received the grand prize of the Intel International Science and Engineering Fair for his invention. Since his success, he has met Bill Clinton and Barack Obama and been interviewed by the BBC, CNN and many other radio stations, television channels and newspapers around the world. Jack hasn't stopped inventing and is currently working with a group of other prize-winning teenagers on a device the size of a mobile phone that can diagnose a wide range of illnesses instantly and without a blood sample. Sounds like something from *Star Trek*, right? Well, yes. That's where the inspiration came from.

6 Professor Maitra is enthusiastic about Jack's future. The professor spoke to a newspaper reporter and compared Jack to Thomas Edison, the inventor of the light bulb. He called him, the Edison of our times, and promised there were going to be a lot of light bulbs coming from Jack in the future.

1 Read the article. Why is it called *A lot of light bulbs*?

1 Because Jack Andraka invented several new types of the light bulb. ☐
2 Because light is an important element in Jack Andraka's invention. ☐
3 Because the writer is comparing Jack to Thomas Edison, the inventor of the light bulb. ☐

2 Read the article again and choose the correct answer, A, B, C or D.

1 In the first paragraph, the writer wants to
A explain how unusual Jack is.
B explain Jack's interest in science.
C describe Jack's personality and looks.
D explain how normal Jack is.

2 Jack began the research into his invention because of
A the death of someone famous.
B an interesting Biology class at school.
C the loss of a friend.
D something he read in a scientific journal.

3 Which organisation helped Jack develop his invention?
A North County High School
B Johns Hopkins School of Medicine
C Apple
D Intel

4 The text says that Jack's test for pancreatic cancer
A doesn't require a blood sample.
B was inspired by *Star Trek*.
C is not as fast as current tests.
D can also help patients with other kinds of cancer.

5 What is the main message of the article?
A Young people can achieve amazing things.
B You don't have to be rich to be a successful inventor.
C Even the most serious types of cancer are treatable.
D Few organisations are willing to help young inventors.

3 Match the headings with the paragraphs of the article. There are two extra headings.

a Development of the test ☐
b An average teenager ☐
c A bright future ☐
d Inspired by *Star Trek* ☐
e Jack's big idea ☐
f Pancreatic cancer ☐
g Recognition for Jack ☐
h Not so normal after all ☐

4 Match these phrasal verbs with their underlined synonyms in the text.

0 carry on *continue*
1 brought up ________
2 came across ________
3 got in touch with ________
4 came up with ________
5 given up ________

5 Complete the sentences with the correct form of the phrasal verbs in Exercise 4.

0 They *carried on* walking until they reached the fence that surrounded the mysterious building.
1 One day, if I become a parent, I hope to ________ my kids in a world where men and women are truly equal.
2 I wasn't planning to buy you a gift, but then I ________ this in the market and I just had to get it.
3 Uncle Steve has ________ smoking four times this year. It's obviously not working.
4 Lindsay ________ the idea for a surprise party for Damien. He absolutely loved it.
5 David, your teacher ________ me today to say that you haven't been to school all week.

REMEMBER BETTER

Draw a line down the page of a notebook to make two columns. In one column write the phrasal verbs from Exercise 4 and in the other column write their full-verb synonyms. Fold the page so that you can only see one of the columns, then test yourself or a friend by trying to remember what is on the other side.

WORD STORE 6E

Word families – health issues

6 For each pair of sentences, complete one gap with the verb and one with the noun form of the words in the box. Change the form of the verbs if necessary.

~~cure~~ diagnose inject prescribe prevent recover treat

0 a Many types of cancer can now be *cured*.
b There is no *cure* for the common cold.
1 a Eat healthily and get plenty of exercise. When it comes to heart disease, ________ is better than cure.
b To ________ the spread of bacteria in the hospital, please wash your hands regularly.
2 a To get an exact ________, we'll have to do a blood test.
b The doctor examined Claire and ________ her illness as a stomach virus.
3 a I'm sorry, sir, you can only buy this medicine if you have a(n) ________ from the doctor.
b You have an ear infection James, so I'm going to ________ a course of antibiotics.
4 a Dear Nicole, get well soon. We hope you have a quick ________. Love from Chris and Mike.
b It may take several months to ________ from a heart attack.
5 a The best ________ for a cold is to rest and drink plenty of fluids.
b Nowadays, doctors can ________ malaria with drugs.
6 a Shelly hates needles in her mouth. ________ at the dentist's are her worst nightmare.
b Ellen, I need to ________ you now, so you might feel just a little pain.

6.5 Grammar

Third Conditional

SHOW WHAT YOU KNOW

1 Complete the beginnings of the sentences with the Past Perfect form of the verbs in brackets. Then match them with the endings.

0 Jack and I *hadn't met* (not meet), [c]
1 Beata ________ (break) her arm once, [ ]
2 Ken ________ (lose) touch with Amy, [ ]
3 Emma ________ (not study) meteorology, [ ]

a so she didn't know a lot about the weather.
b so she knew how much it hurt.
c so I didn't recognise him.
d so he was surprised when she called.

2 ★ Read the sentences and choose the correct options.

1 If Jack and I had met, I would've recognised him.
real past event: We *met / didn't meet*.
real past result: I *recognised / didn't recognise* him.

2 Beata wouldn't have known how much it hurts when you break your arm if she hadn't done it once.
real past event: Beata *broke / didn't break* her arm once.
real past result: She *knew / didn't know* how much it hurt.

3 Ken wouldn't have been surprised when Amy called if he hadn't lost touch with her.
real past event: Ken *lost touch / didn't lose touch* with Amy.
real past result: He *was / wasn't* surprised when she called.

4 Emma would have known a lot about the weather if she had studied meteorology.
real past event: Emma *studied / didn't study* meteorology.
real past result: She *knew / didn't know* a lot about the weather.

3 ★★ Complete the conversation with the correct form of the verbs in brackets. Use short forms.

Anne and Dan are at the summer house.

A: What a long journey. Open the door, Dan. I need a cup of tea.
D: You've got the keys.
A: What? I texted you this morning to say bring the spare ones.
D: What? If I [0] *'d received* (receive) a text message, my phone [1] ________ (go) beep.
A: Well, I definitely texted you. You [2] ________ (see) the message if you [3] ________ (look) at your phone. I've lost my keys.
D: But why didn't you say something before we left? Anne, we are 200km from home!
A: We'll have to break a window.

Later in the hospital:

D: Ouch! This really hurt, Nurse!
N: Sorry, Mr Finch, but I have to clean the cut.
A: I'm sorry, Dan.
D: It's not your fault, Anne.
A: But if I [4] ________ (not lose) the keys, you [5] ________ (not cut) your hand and we wouldn't be here in the hospital now.

4 ★★★ Write Third Conditional sentences to complete the conversations.

0 **Erin:** I was in a bad mood last night. I shouted at Sally and we had an argument.
Alfie: stay calm / not fall out
Oh dear! If *you'd stayed calm, you wouldn't have fallen out*.

1 **Karen:** I was late home last night. Mum was so mad.
Nina: phone your mum / she probably not be so angry
Oh Karen! If ________________ .

2 **Dominic:** I really thought I'd left my passport at home.
Reece: miss the flight / you forget it
We ________________ .

3 **Louis:** Chris fell off his bike yesterday. The bruise on his forehead was huge.
Imogen: not hurt himself / wear his helmet
It's his own fault, Louis. He ________________ ________________ .

4 **Jodie:** That food was so spicy.
Issac: not be so bad / not used so much chilli sauce
It ________________ .

SHOW WHAT YOU'VE LEARNT

5 Complete the Third Conditional sentences. Use *if* and the prompts in brackets.

0 We wouldn't have won (you / not score / a goal).
We wouldn't have won if *you hadn't scored a goal* .

1 (you / not be / cold) if you had worn long trousers that night.
________________ you had worn long trousers.

2 If the clothes hadn't been so cheap, (I / not buy / three jackets).
If the clothes hadn't been so cheap, ________________ .

3 My boyfriend would have left me if (I / forget / about his birthday again).
My boyfriend would have left me ________________ .

4 (our electricity bill / be / smaller) last year if we'd bought low-energy light bulbs.
________________ last year if we'd bought low-energy light bulbs.

5 Daisy wouldn't have burnt herself if (she / be / more careful in the kitchen).
Daisy wouldn't have burnt herself ________________ .

/5

6.6 Speaking language practice

A doctor's appointment

1 Put the words in 1–5 in the correct order to form questions. Then match them with answers a–f.

0 pain / when / start / the / did?
When did the pain start? [f]

1 other / have / do / symptoms / you / any?
______ [ ]

2 does / if / push / I / here / hurt / it?
______ [ ]

3 dizzy / you / feel / do?
______ [ ]

4 ever / you / rash / had / a / have?
______ [ ]

5 time / when / were / was / last / the / you / ill?
______ [ ]

a About six months ago. I had a bad cough.
b Yes, as well as the headache, I feel sick.
c No, never. This is the first time.
d Yes, it feels like the room is spinning.
e Ouch! Yes, it does.
f Yesterday, when I got home from school.

2 Cross out the option that is not possible in each sentence. Then write *D* for something a doctor would say or *P* for something a patient would say.

1 I'm going to *give you a prescription / give you indigestion / make an appointment for you.* [ ]
2 I feel *ill / weak / temperature.* [ ]
3 I've got a *sick / sore throat / runny nose.* [ ]
4 I'm going to *examine you / take your temperature / lie down please.* [ ]
5 I think you've got *a virus / a blood test / indigestion.* [ ]
6 You should *open wide / eat more slowly / go on a diet.* [ ]
7 Breathe *in / out / down.* [ ]

3 Put the conversation in the correct order.

[1] Good morning. Please come in and sit down. Max, is it?
[ ] Well, let's take a look. Lie down, please. If I push here does it hurt?
[ ] Yes, I've got a runny nose and a sore throat and I feel very weak.
[ ] Actually, no. Not there either.
[ ] I think I'm dying, doctor. I feel terrible and I've got an awful headache.
[ ] Yes, doctor. Max Cooper.
[ ] Dying? Oh dear! Do you have any other symptoms?
[ ] Well, no. No, it doesn't.
[ ] OK, Max, what seems to be the problem?
[ ] Well, Max, I don't think you are going to die just yet. I think perhaps you have a cold.
[ ] And here?

REMEMBER THIS

Ouch is a word for the sound that you make when you feel sudden pain. Such sounds are called interjections. Other examples include ***achoo***, the sound of a sneeze, ***oops***, a sound you make when you make a mistake or break or drop something, ***phew***, a sound to express relief, and ***wow***, a sound to express amazement. Look in a dictionary or online for more interjections like these.

4 Isobel is at the doctor's. Complete the words in the conversation. The first letter of each word is given.

D: Isobel? Yes, come in, please. Have a seat. How can I help?
I: Sorry?
D: Isobel, is it? Please sit down. How can I help?
I: Yes, thanks. I'm Isobel.
D: Er … yes … well. [0]**W***hat's* **t***he* **p***roblem*, Isobel?
I: Well, my ears [1]**h**_____ and I can't hear very well.
D: Aha! I see. Do you have any other symptoms?
I: Yes, [2]I **f**_____ **d**_____, like my head is spinning, and my neck is [3]**s**_____. It's much bigger than usual.
D: Yes, I can see that. [4]**W**_____ **d**_____ **t**_____ **p**_____ **s**_____?
I: Sorry?
D: How long have you been in pain?
I: In Spain? I've never been to Spain.
D: No, WHEN DID IT START HURTING?
I: Oh, sorry. Yesterday.
D: OK, er … since Thursday.
I: No, thanks.
D: What?
I: No, thanks, I'm not thirsty.
D: No, I said SINCE THURSDAY.
I: Oh yes. I was looking after my little sister and I fell asleep and when I woke up, I couldn't hear properly.
D: I see. [5]**I**_____ **g**_____ **t**_____ **e**_____ **y**_____.
Lie [6]**d**_____, **p**_____.
Aha! [7]I **t**_____ **y**_____ **g**_____ something stuck in your ear. Yes, and in this side too. Hang on. I'll pull them.
I: Ouch!
D: Well, how strange. These look like little round sweets.
I: What? How did they get in there?
D: Perhaps you need to speak to your little sister.
I: She must have … I'll kill her!

6.7 Writing

An article

1 Match the sentence halves to make tips for writing an article.

1 Give your article an interesting or funny title ☐
2 Try to avoid repeating the same words ☐
3 Talk directly to the reader in the article ☐
4 Use linking expressions ☐

a by using a wide range of vocabulary.
b to make well-constructed and logical sentences.
c to attract reader's attention.
d by asking some questions.

2 Match the examples with the tips in Exercise 1. There are two examples for one of the tips.

a How many diets have you tried? I've been on loads!
b As well as having a degree in medicine, Jack has several years of experience as a volunteer.
c My (un)healthy life!
d Katy loved studying to be a doctor. She particularly enjoyed her second year.
e When I was a child, I always saw the same doctor whereas now I see a different doctor every time I'm ill!

3 Read the article and put the paragraphs in the correct order (1–4). Then choose the best title.

A ___ B ___ C ___ D ___

1 My sister had an accident in France
2 Doctor! Doctor!
3 Don't go swimming!
4 How to treat a foot injury

A We were spending the day on a beautiful sandy beach and my sister went swimming. Then she came out of the water. She was crying and she couldn't walk very well. Her foot was very red and it was getting bigger and bigger as we looked. What should we do next?

B This taught us an important lesson. People really need to find out before they go on holiday what to do and where to go in a medical emergency!

C Getting ill is horrible, but somehow it's even worse when you're on holiday. It can also be really scary because you're not always sure what to do! Something bad happened to my young sister when our family was on holiday in the north of France. It scared us all.

D Luckily, there was a French woman near us on the beach. She pointed across the road and said, 'Doctor, doctor! Quick!' Dad carried my sister to the house the woman pointed at and a doctor saw my sister immediately. He said that she had stepped on a dangerous fish and he gave her an injection. Her foot got better within a few minutes!

SHOW WHAT YOU'VE LEARNT

4 You have seen this announcement on an international students' website.

Holiday health problems!

Have you ever been ill on holiday or do you know someone who has? We are looking for articles about people's experiences. Write an article about getting ill on holiday, saying how people helped you, and you could see your article on the website!

Write your article in 140–190 words.

SHOW THAT YOU'VE CHECKED

In my article:

- I have used a catchy title. ☐
- I have engaged the reader by addressing them directly sometimes. ☐
- I have shown a range of vocabulary and avoided repeating words. ☐
- I have used linking words. ☐
- I have written an ending that is funny or interesting. ☐
- I have checked my spelling and punctuation. ☐
- I have written at least 140 words. ☐

6.8 Use of English

Multiple-choice cloze

1 For questions 1–8, read the article below and decide which answer (A, B, C or D) best fits each gap. There is an example at the beginning.

The Loch Ness Challenge

Have you ever heard of Scotland's Loch Ness Monster? Well, this year I took part [0]__ a different kind of Loch Ness Monster: it was a 'monster' charity cycle race – 106 kilometres long!

The event is held every year and [1]__ cycle around the lake on traffic-free roads. The idea of the race is to [2]__ money for the cancer support charity Macmillan. I decided to do the race in [3]__ of my grandfather, who died from cancer two years ago. I asked all my friends and family to [4]__ me for as much money as they could. In the end, we were able to [5]__ over £400 to Macmillan. The best way to organise and collect the money is to [6]__ up a webpage through a specially-designed website. There are loads of them on the Internet.

A word or warning: I would have done more training if I [7]__ known how steep some of the hills were! My ankles and feet were [8]__ by the end of the day (they soon went back to their normal size, you'll be pleased to know!).

Would I do it again? Of course! In fact, I've already entered next year's race. Maybe I'll see you there!

	A	B	C	D
0	A of	(B in)	C on	D at
1	A supporters	B members	C participants	D public
2	A raise	B provide	C have	D bring
3	A reminder	B reminding	C remembering	D memory
4	A suggest	B recommend	C offer	D sponsor
5	A help	B pass	C donate	D award
6	A make	B set	C take	D use
7	A had	B am	C have	D was
8	A scratched	B swollen	C broken	D dislocated

TIPS:

Question 1: Which word describes people who are doing sporting events?
Question 2: You need a word that collocates with *money* and describes what people do for charities.
Question 3: Look at the words before and after the gap. Only one of the words can complete the phrase.

Open cloze

2 For questions 1–9, read the email below and think of the word which best fits each gap. There is an example at the beginning.

Hi Anna,

I have an amazing story to tell you! I'm actually [0] *in* hospital at the moment. It's OK, don't [1]__________ . I'm OK now, but let me tell you what happened.

I was out for a picnic in the countryside with my family when I started finding it difficult to breathe. I've had hay [2]__________ for years, especially in the spring and summer. With that, though, I usually only get a [3]__________ nose (I use so many tissues!) rather than breathing problems. My mum said I had all the symptoms [4]__________ asthma, but I'd never had that before. Eventually, Mum decided to take me to the hospital. The doctor did a blood [5]__________ but there didn't seem to be anything wrong. It hurt [6]__________ she took the blood, but it wasn't as bad as having an [7]__________ . You know I hate having a needle stuck in my arm! But guess who's just arrived at the hospital and is sitting here with me now! Jenny! She's broken her leg, so she's a patient [8]__________ the hospital too. They put her in the bed next to mine. I wish you [9]__________ here with us too. But don't have an accident! By the way, my asthma's OK and I should be out soon.

See you soon!

Maria

TIPS:

Question 1: You need the base form of a verb here.
Question 2: What collocates with *hay* and is a condition a lot of people get in the spring and summer?
Question 3: What word describes your nose when you need to use a lot of tissues?

6.9 Self-assessment

1 For each learning objective, tick the box that best matches your ability.

☺☺ = I understand and can help a friend.
☺ = I understand and can do it by myself.
☹ = I understand some, but have some questions.
☹☹ = I do not understand.

			☺☺	☺	☹	☹☹	Need help?
6.1	Vocabulary	I can talk about the body and minor injuries.					Students' Book pages 72–73 Word Store page 13 Workbook pages 68–69
6.2	Grammar	I can talk about imaginary situations in the present.					Students' Book page 74 Workbook page 70
6.3	Listening	I can identify details in conversations and talks.					Students' Book page 75 Workbook page 71
6.4	Reading	I can find specific detail in an article.					Students' Book pages 76–77 Workbook pages 72–73
6.5	Grammar	I can talk about imaginary situations in the past.					Students' Book page 78 Workbook page 74
6.6	Speaking	I can talk about health, illness, symptoms and treatment.					Students' Book page 79 Workbook page 75
6.7	Writing	I can write an article for a student magazine.					Students' Book pages 80–81 Workbook page 76

2 What can you remember from this unit?

New words I learned (the words you most want to remember from this unit)	**Expressions and phrases I liked** (any expressions or phrases you think sound nice, useful or funny)	**English I heard or read outside class** (e.g. from websites, books, adverts, films, music)

6.10 Self-check

1 Complete the sentences with the correct form of the words in the box. There are two extra words.

eye hand heart jaw
leg ~~lip~~ thumb thigh

0 Be careful not to burn your *lips* – this tea is really hot.
1 I wasn't serious! I was only pulling your ________ .
2 When Simon kissed Polly, he broke Sue's ________ .
3 Leah needs some help with her Maths homework. Can you give her a(n) ________ ?
4 I don't like these jeans. They're the wrong shape for my legs. They make my ________ look really big.
5 Sam's ring is too big for his fingers, so he has to wear it on his ________ .

/5

2 Match the words in box A with the words in box B. Then complete the sentences. There is an extra word in box A.

A black ear first hay ~~dislocated~~ nose sun

B aid burn eye fever ache ~~shoulder~~

0 After the rugby match we discovered that Andrew had a(n) *dislocated shoulder* .
1 When Scott took off his sunglasses, everyone was shocked to see that he had a(n) ____________ .
2 Don't go swimming if you have a(n) ____________ . It'll get worse if water gets in there.
3 Achoo! Oh, excuse me. I get ____________ at this time of year. I'm allergic to the summer grasses.
4 Oh Mia, look at you. You are bright red! Is it ____________ ? Did you fall asleep by the pool again?
5 Does anyone here know how to give ____________ ? My boyfriend has been stung by a bee.

/5

3 Choose the correct answer, A, B or C.

0 About one minute after the dentist __ the anaesthetic, I couldn't feel the left side of my face.
A sprained B operated (C injected)
1 Jo fell off her horse. She was lucky she didn't __ her neck.
A cut B break C recover
2 We are going to __ this infection with antibiotics and you should feel better in about a week.
A treat B diagnose C prevent
3 When I told Sarah what had happened, she __ her head off. I didn't expect her to find it so funny.
A pulled B broke C laughed
4 Karen found it difficult to walk in high-heels and unfortunately she fell and __ her ankle.
A sprained B scratched C burnt
5 What if the __ for cancer is inside the mind of someone who doesn't have the opportunity for a good education?
A prescription B prevention C cure

/5

4 Complete the sentences with the correct form of the verbs in brackets.

0 I wish I *wasn't* (not be) so tired because I'd really love to go out tonight.
1 If Claire ______ (not feel) ill, she'd join us.
2 Damien wishes he ______ (have) more money so he could take Nicole to an expensive restaurant.
3 If motorists ______ (not drive) so close to each other on the motorway, there would be far fewer accidents.
4 If the government made healthcare free for everyone in the country, we ______ (pay) much higher taxes.
5 If only ice cream ______ (be) good for me. I'd be the healthiest person alive.

/5

5 Decide which prompt goes in each gap. Then complete the Third Conditional sentences. Use short forms.

0 Jack *wouldn't have been late* if he *hadn't stopped* to watch the football match. (not be late, not stop)
1 Erin ____________ the other skier if she ____________ so quickly. (hit, not turn)
2 I ____________ to pay for everyone if I ____________ how expensive it was here. (know, not offer)
3 If Jill ____________ her shoulder, she ____________ in the match yesterday. (dislocate, not play)
4 If Connor ____________ to the toilets, he ____________ in the classroom. (not run, be sick)
5 The doctor ____________ penicillin for Fay if she ____________ she was allergic to it. (not say, prescribe)

/5

6 Read the email and choose the correct answer, A, B or C.

Hi Clara,

I'm writing to you from my hospital bed after the [0]___ on my knee. I'm doing OK, but it is still a bit painful. They [1]___ a big hole in my leg (!) and it's going to take a while to [2]___ . I asked if I could go home this morning. The doctor said that if I went home, I [3]___ the strong painkillers they give me here. He says I need to stay for another two days. I wish I [4]___ because I miss normal food. If Mum [5]___ me food from home, I wouldn't have eaten anything this week. Are you coming to visit me tomorrow? If you do, can you bring me some magazines?

See you x

	A	B	C
0	(A operation)	B fever	C patient
1	A bruised	B cut	C stung
2	A cure	B treat	C recover
3	A wouldn't get	B won't get	C didn't get
4	A can leave	B could leave	C left
5	A didn't bring	B wouldn't bring	C hadn't brought

/5

Total /30

7 IN THE SPOTLIGHT

7.1 Vocabulary

Television • Modifiers with base and extreme adjectives

SHOW WHAT YOU KNOW

1 Match six of the TV programmes in 1–11 with extracts A–F.

0 a sports programme F
1 a talent show
2 a soap opera
3 a music programme
4 the news or current affairs
5 a quiz or game show
6 a chat show
7 the weather
8 a reality show
9 a sitcom
10 a series/serial
11 a documentary

A Later in the programme, the very talented Pharrel Williams will be singing live in the studio. But first, the UK's top ten album downloads this week. At number 10 …

B **Ladies and gentlemen, the lovely Jennifer Lawrence! Jennifer, welcome to the show. Let's start by talking about your latest film ...**

C The time is 6 o'clock and here are today's headlines. The European Union is considering …

D **Question 3 for £2,000: in which country are Christmas gifts given on 24 December rather than 25? The UK, Poland, France or Australia?**

E **After the tiger, the African lion is the second largest of the four big cats, with some males weighing up to 250 kilos.**

F If you've just joined us, the score is 3-2 to Germany and this is turning out to be a fantastic game.

WORD STORE 7A
TV shows

2 Complete the advertisement with the correct form of one of the words in brackets.

Talented Britain

Talented Britain is coming to a city near you soon! Channel 7 is beginning its search for [0] contestants (view / contest) to appear on the next series of *Talented Britain*, which will be [1] ________ (broadcast / perform) next year. Do you have what it takes to perform in front of a(n) [2] ________ (panels / audience) of judges and millions of [3] ________ (act / view) watching at home? This summer we will be holding [4] ________ (rehearse / audition) in towns and cities across the country, so come and prove that you are good enough to be on the show. Start your [5] ________ (broadcast / rehearse) now so you are ready to perform at your best when *Talented Britain* comes to your city.

Click here for a list of cities and dates.

WORD STORE 7B
Word families – TV shows

3 Complete the table.

	Noun		Noun (person)		Verb
	competition		competitor	0	compete
1	________		editor		edit
	entertainment	2	________		entertain
	performance	3	________		perform
	presentation		presenter	4	________
5	________		producer		produce

4 Complete the sentences with words from Exercise 3. The number of letters is given in brackets.

0 Here's Jill, the first of our six competitors on today's show. (11 letters)
1 Nicholas, you ________ on stage regularly, but this is your first film. (7 letters)
2 Here at Granada Studios we ________ two sitcoms and a soap opera. (7 letters)
3 And now, ________ for all the family in our afternoon film *Ice Age 4*. (13 letters)
4 After filming has finished, the ________ begins putting the various scenes together. (6 letters)
5 Natalie desperately wants to become a TV ________ one day. (9 letters)

WORD STORE 7C

Modifiers with base and extreme adjectives

5 Look at the meanings in brackets and complete the extreme adjectives in the conversations. The first letter of each adjective is given.

1 A: Well, that was really **a**wful (very unpleasant)! What a terrible programme and a complete waste of an hour of my life!
B: Well, it's **r**_________ (very silly) to complain now, after you've watched the whole show. Why didn't you switch off after five minutes?

2 A: Did you see *House* last night? Oh, I love it. I think that English guy, the main actor, is absolutely **h**_________ (very funny).
B: *House*? Er, hello? *House* is, like, so old now, and anyway, if you ask me, every episode is **i**_________ (very similar).
A: Yeah, well, whatever. I like it.

3 A: Kyle, TV off! Homework! Now!
B: Dad, I'm watching a documentary about World War II, which is not only **f**_________ (very interesting) but also **e**_________ (very important) for my History project.
A: Oh. Very good, carry on.

4 A: Dad, are you watching the news again? Nothing new has happened since an hour ago.
B: Toby, new things happen all the time. There's just been an **a**_________ (very good) report about a skateboarding dog.
A: Er … sounds great.
C: Don't listen to your dad. He's only watching because he thinks the newsreader is **g**_________ (very beautiful).
B: That's not true! Well, I mean, she's quite pretty, yes, but she's also a **b**_________ (very talented) journalist.
B: Who reports on skateboarding dogs …
A: Don't you have some homework to do, Toby?

6 Write the modifiers in the box in the correct place on the line.

absolutely   not very   rather   really   very

100% ← _________
← _________
← _________

← _________
← quite
← _________
0% ← absolutely not

7 Read the text and choose the correct options.

Telly Addicts: last night on the box

Here at Telly Addicts we thought last night's television highlight was definitely the [1]*absolutely / rather* fascinating BBC2 documentary *Icemen* about the lives of Iceland's fishermen. Some of the fishermen's stories were [2]*rather / absolutely* sad, but [3]*very / absolutely* interesting, and the shots of the Icelandic coastline were [4]*very / absolutely* gorgeous.

Also worth watching was Channel 4's new quiz *What's Up?* which was presented by the [5]*extremely / absolutely* talented Rosie Perks and her [6]*very / absolutely* funny partner Richard Bond. Though many of the questions on the show are [7]*very / absolutely* impossible to answer, we still found it [8]*really / absolutely* entertaining from start to finish.

SHOW WHAT YOU'VE LEARNT

8 Choose the correct answer, A, B or C.

1 Hello, everyone. I'm Serge Dupont. Today *Channel 8 News* is ___ live from outside the European Parliament.
A broadcasting B rehearsing C auditioning

2 Next, a ___ of experts discuss the results of today's election in our Election Special.
A contestant B panel C viewer

3 Katy, you're a world-famous ___ . You sing, you dance, you act and now you've written a book. Is there anything you can't do?
A performer B editor C producer

4 I've always wanted to ___ people. At school I used to tell jokes and sing songs in front of the class.
A compete B present C entertain

5 And now a special celebrity Christmas ___ of *Who wants to be a Millionaire?*
A entertainment B edition C competition

6 Big Don is an extremely ___ character. He's certainly not popular with viewers.
A impossible B brilliant C unpleasant

7 If you ask me, the story has become ___ ridiculous. I think I'm going to stop watching this series.
A very B extremely C absolutely

8 The news is very ___ on all the channels. It doesn't make much difference which one you watch.
A identical B similar C awful

9 We finally watched *One Flew over the Cuckoo's Nest* last night. What an absolutely ___ film!
A amazing B important C interesting

10 Remember the ___ where the monkey suddenly jumped out of the trees? I jumped a metre out of my seat.
A series B scene C serial

/10

7.2 Grammar

Reported Speech – statements

SHOW WHAT YOU KNOW

1 Put the words in the correct order to complete the conversation between Mum, Dad and Kristy.

D: Kirsty, please tell me we are not watching *The X Factor*.
K: You [1]____________ (watch / said / could / I) it tonight.
D: No, I [2]____________ (could / you / watch / said) it upstairs.
K: Dad!
D: What? The other day I [3]____________ (I / television / said / was / taking back / my) on Saturday nights. I want to watch the Grand Prix.
K: Mum! *The X Factor* has started!
D: Kirsty! Last Saturday night I [4]____________ (told / you / bought / I / had) a second television for exactly this kind of situation.
M: Oh. Did you [5]____________ (*The X Factor* / that / say / started / had) ?
D: But ... the Grand Prix.
M: There's another television upstairs, Walter.

2 ★ Report the underlined statements.

0 Charles Sykes: 'Television is not real life. In real life people actually have to leave the coffee shop and go to real jobs.'
Charles Sykes said that television was not real life .

1 Ann Landers: 'Television has proved that people will look at anything rather than each other.'
Ann Landers said that ________________________ rather than each other.

2 Kevin O'Leary: 'Television is the most interesting hobby I have ever had.'
Kevin O'Leary said ________________________ .

3 Margaret Mead: 'Thanks to television, the young are seeing history before it is censored by their elders.'
Margaret Mead said that thanks to television, ________________________ by their elders.

3 ★★ Match the underlined reporting verbs in the report with the definitions which follow.

Minister Embarrassed in Television Interview

Last night on *Channel 10 News* the Minister for Culture claimed that young people were happier these days than when he had been young. The journalist Mandy Striker pointed out that there was no real proof of that and politely suggested that happiness was very difficult to measure. The minister explained that his statement was based on meetings he had had with young people and parents in local schools in his area. He added that his own teenage children were also living full and happy lives. The minister then asked Ms Striker if this was reasonable evidence. Ms Striker replied that not all young people were as lucky as those who lived in the area where the minister lived.

0 gave a reason for something explained
1 said that something was true __________
2 answered __________
3 said more about something __________
4 told someone something that they didn't know or hadn't thought of __________
5 said something in an indirect way __________

4 ★★★ Read the statements and choose the correct reporting verbs. Then complete the reported statements.

0 'Honestly, please believe me, I really didn't know she was a drug dealer.'
The TV presenter *suggested* / *claimed* he hadn't known (not know) that the woman had been a drug dealer. He begged the court to believe him.

1 'In our opinion, the show isn't suitable for children.'
When a journalist asked why the show had been banned, the members of the panel *added* / *replied* that, in _______ opinion, it _______ (not be) suitable for children.

2 'Don't tell everyone, but maybe you should wait until next week. There's probably going to be a sale here.'
I was in the electrical store a few weeks ago and the assistant winked at me and *replied* / *suggested* that the _______ week there _______ (probably/be) a sale _______ .

3 'Leo can't have taken the car today. My car keys are still here.'
I was at Maggie's house last week when her car was stolen. I *added* / *suggested* that maybe Leo had taken it, but she said Leo _______ (not take) the car _______ day because _______ keys were _______ .

SHOW WHAT YOU'VE LEARNT

5 Report the statements.

0 'I'll miss the last part of my favourite TV series tomorrow.'
It was a long time ago, but I remember she said she would miss the last part of her favourite TV series the following day .

1 'We're going to be on television next week.'
Two months ago, they said ________________ .

2 'I'm meeting your sister here later today.'
We were in the café and Dad told me ________________ .

3 'We saw you both last month.'
It was back in January when they told us ________________ .

4 'Your audition is cancelled.'
We waited all day, then at 6 o'clock in the evening the organiser told us that ________________ .

5 'I'll see you tomorrow.'
Six days ago she told him she ________________ , but then she never came back.

/5

7.3 Listening language practice

Useful expressions • Synonyms • Words with two meanings

1 Read the extracts and complete the phrases in bold with the words in the box. Then listen and check.

common	expression	feel	~~formula~~
himself	laugh	spans	stupid

Extract from Students' Book recording CD•3.24 MP3•113

1

A viral video is a video that becomes popular very quickly through the Internet. People share the video through social media and email. There isn't **a** [0]*formula* **for** a viral video hit. But the most popular ones **have three things in** [1]_______. Firstly, they're really <u>short</u>. People **have short attention** [2]_______, especially when they're looking at websites, so the most successful viral videos are around three minutes long. Secondly, they engage your emotions; they may be <u>funny</u>, sad, <u>shocking</u>, entertaining or even extremely <u>annoying</u>, but they **make viewers** [3]_______ **something**. The third ingredient is story. Many of the most popular viral videos tell a <u>simple</u> story and the ones with an inspirational ending are the most memorable.

3

My favourite videos are the ones that **make you** [4]_______. It's usually because somebody **does something** [5]_______. For instance, there's a video of a man who dives into a frozen swimming pool. Well, I say he dives, but of course, he hits the ice and slides across the swimming pool. How can you be so <u>stupid</u>? […] I couldn't believe it! And I love the one where a baby bites his brother's finger. The little brother puts his finger in his baby brother's mouth and, **surprise, surprise,** the baby bites it. I love **the** [6]_______ **on the baby's face – he's very** <u>pleased</u> **with** [7]_______.

2 Complete the sentences with words and phrases from Exercise 1. Change the verb forms if necessary.

0 People ask me what the formula *for* success is. I tell them it's hard work and good timing.
1 Viv loves spending time with Dave. He _______ her feel happy and relaxed.
2 I love visual comedy. It _______ me laugh more than any joke could.
3 Emma and Karen both got top marks in the test, so they were very _______ with themselves.
4 When Kieran heard he had won, the expression _______ his face was fantastic.
5 Danielle, I've _______ something really stupid. I forgot to pay the deposit and we've lost the booking.
6 Lindsay and I split up. We just didn't have anything _______ common.
7 This game is for children over six. Younger children's attention spans are too _______ to enjoy it.

3 Match the underlined adjectives in the extracts with their synonyms.

0 happy *pleased*
1 brief _______
2 amusing _______
3 straight-forward _______
4 foolish _______
5 irritating _______
6 disturbing _______

4 Read REMEMBER THIS. Which meaning of *surprise, surprise* is used in extract 2 in Exercise 1?

REMEMBER THIS

The expression ***surprise, surprise*** can be used when something unexpected and pleasant happens.
I asked her out on a date and, surprise, surprise, she actually said yes!

In contrast, it is often used ironically, when someone has done something or something has happened that was very predictable and therefore is not a surprise.
He was late on Monday and Tuesday and, surprise, surprise, he was late again on Wednesday.

WORD STORE 7D
Words with two meanings

5 Choose the correct answer, A, B or C, to complete both sentences in each pair.

1 Gary, you've had four ___ singles this year and your album is number one in the charts.
I posted a video of myself dancing on Tumblr, but it hasn't had even one ___ so far.
A big B view C hit

2 Click on the ___ below for more information.
People have known about the ___ between smoking and health problems for decades.
A page B connection C link

3 The doctor said it was a ___ infection, so antibiotics wouldn't help.
This year's most popular ___ video on YouTube featured a talking dog.
A serious B viral C short

4 In my ___, most of the programmes on television are rubbish.
My website had a(n) ___ from someone in Alaska yesterday!
A opinion B view C hit

5 I wasn't very hungry, so I ___ my sandwich with Helen.
You ___ a photo on your profile. Click here to tag the people in the photo.
A shared B divided C split

6 Will you ___ this letter for me if you pass a box?
That is a hilarious video. I'm going to ___ it on Facebook.
A post B send C put

7.4 Reading

The story behind your TV set • Collocations • Phrasal verbs

Glossary

dial (n) = the wheel-like part of a radio or old-fashioned television that you turn to find a different station or channel
adjust (v) = to change or move something slightly to improve it or make it work better

1 Read the article. For questions 1–7, choose from the sections (A–E). You can choose each section more than once.

Which section mentions:

1 an activity that was unreliable? ☐
2 a way of locating the correct channels? ☐
3 one gadget that has replaced several other gadgets? ☐
4 the weight of an early television? ☐
5 a means of finding out what is on television? ☐
6 a reminder that the gadgets we use today will continue to change? ☐
7 a part of an early television that was not easy to use? ☐

The story behind your TV set

A

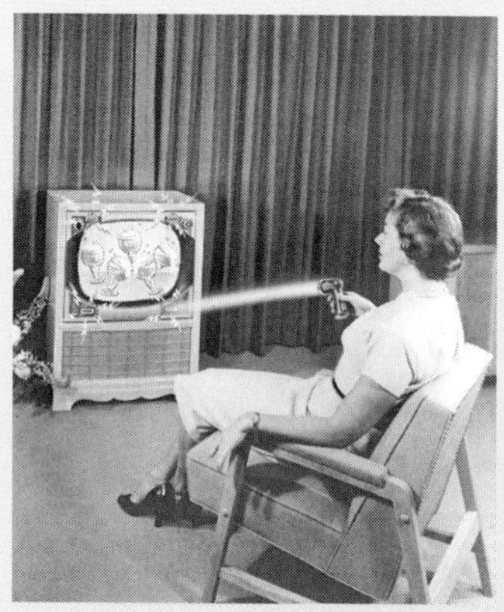

If your mum or dad were lucky enough to have a television in their bedroom when they were your age, they probably felt pretty cool, even if it was black and white, weighed about twenty kilos and had an antenna that looked like a metal coat hanger. 1____ The technology of televisions has changed so quickly that it's not surprising some of the most sophisticated features of the TV sets of the past seem rather silly these days. In this week's article, check out these old TV technologies, but while you are laughing, remember that many modern gadgets will seem just as ridiculous to the youngsters of tomorrow.

B

Stay tuned is something you still occasionally hear people on television say when they are really asking you not to switch off or change the channel. The phrase has lost its original meaning, which referred to 'tuning' early analogue televisions (adjusting them to get the best quality picture) by turning a big dial, or wheel, on the front. Later televisions had individual channel buttons, but for each button there was still a tuning dial located behind a little plastic door on the front of the set. These dials were often tiny and tricky to turn, so some manufacturers used to sell their sets with a little plastic stick that you would put into a hole and turn until the picture was clear enough to watch. 2____ Nowadays, thank goodness, televisions 'tune' themselves automatically.

C

When your parents were young, 'channel surfing' actually required physical effort because to change the channel, you had to stand up, walk across the room and press a button on the television. 3____ Eventually, remote controls were invented, but the first ones actually had a wire that stretched across the room from the remote to the television. Later more boxes appeared – video recorders, satellite tuners and so on – and with those came additional remote controls. Eventually, when it became impossible to open the living room door because of all the different remotes, universal controllers became popular and one small device could finally control all the different boxes in your living room! Now, with the help of the right app, it is becoming more and more common to use a mobile phone or tablet to control all the various media devices in your house, though some homes still have more remote controls than hands to operate them.

D

Not so many years ago, viewers had no choice but to wait a week for the next episode of their favourite TV programmes to be shown. 4____ It was not unusual for people to plan their week around the TV schedule and, if they were busy at the time of their favourite show, they either missed it or found space on a video tape, set the video recorder for the right time and hoped the tape didn't run out before the programme had finished. These days, TV schedules are still printed in magazines and some newspapers. However, they are much less significant because of 'catch-up' TV channels, on-demand Internet TV services such as Netflix or I-player and, of course, legal and illegal downloading.

E

Television and the technology associated with it is changing constantly and if you have children, by the time they are your age, flat-screen, HD and 3D will probably seem as silly and old-fashioned as black and white, two channels only and a coat hanger for an aerial.

2 Read the article again. Choose from the sentences (A–E) the one which fits each gap (1–5). There is one extra sentence.

A If you lost this little tool, the entire set became useless. ☐

B These first colour television sets were extremely expensive. ☐

C People would check the weekly TV schedule in a magazine or newspaper and highlight the shows they really wanted to watch. ☐

D Now, just a decade or two later, most of us carry small, powerful, high-definition, full-colour, multi-media devices in our bags and pockets. ☐

E Actually, this wasn't such a big problem, because for a long time there were only two or three channels to choose from. ☐

3 Match the underlined adjectives in the article with their synonyms below. Use a dictionary if necessary.

0 fortunate = *lucky*		4 single	= _______
1 important	= _______	5 instant	= _______
2 advanced	= _______	6 contemporary	= _______
3 more	= _______	7 difficult	= _______

REMEMBER BETTER

When you learn a new word or if you want to learn more about a word you already know, look it up in a dictionary and make a note of some common collocations in which it is used.

Complete each group of sentences with one of the underlined adjectives in the article.

0 a And the *lucky* **winner** of tonight's lottery is ticket number 459!

b That was a(n) *lucky* **escape**. If we hadn't been late, we would've been on the train that crashed.

c Did you really know the answer or was it a *lucky* **guess**?

1 a Jolanta thought number 7 was a particularly _______ **question**.

b It's a bit of a(n) _______ **situation**. If I go to the party, I'll have to talk to my ex-boyfriend; but if I don't go, I won't see any of my friends.

c For many young people, love can be a very _______ **subject** to discuss with parents.

2 a There has been a(n) _______ **increase** in the price of tropical fruit recently.

b Obviously, there is a(n) _______ **difference** in the quality of the picture on a television which costs €1,000 and one which costs €100.

c Environmentalists have noted _______ **changes** in the temperature of sea water in this area.

3 a In the _______ **world** most people have access to television.

b Computers are an essential part of _______ **life**.

c Have you been to the Museum of _______ **Art**?

WORD STORE 7E
Phrasal verbs

4 Complete the second sentence using the word in capitals so that it has a similar meaning to the first. Do not change the word in capitals.

0 I found an interesting vlog by a DJ the other day. **ACROSS**
I *came across* an interesting vlog by a DJ the other day.

1 Jake became interested in skateboarding when he was four. **INTO**
Jake _____________ skateboarding when he was four.

2 The bill for the school's new computer room totalled €26,000. **CAME**
The bill for the school's new computer room _____________ €26,000.

3 The new smartphone did not match the telecommunications industry's expectations. **LIVE**
The new smartphone did not _____________ the telecommunications industry's expectations.

4 If I don't continue to do the cleaning, the bathroom becomes too disgusting to use. **KEEP**
If I don't _____________ the cleaning, the bathroom becomes too disgusting to use.

5 They really need to think of a new type of reality show. I'm so bored with singing competitions. **WITH**
They really need to _____________ a new type of reality show. I'm so bored with singing competitions.

7.5 Grammar

Reported Speech – questions and imperatives

SHOW WHAT YOU KNOW

1 Read Lori's answers and write her grandmother's questions.

G: 0 *What are you going to wear to the end-of-term party?*
L: I'm going to wear a black dress and high heels to the end-of-term party.
G: 1 ______
L: I'm going with my friends and my boyfriend.
G: 2 ______
L: Yes, I have got a boyfriend, Grandma.
G: 3 ______
L: I started seeing him last month.
G: 4 ______
L: Yes, he's good to me.
G: 5 ______
L: You're going to meet him at my birthday party.

2 ★ Katy is talking to her friend about a boy she met in a café yesterday. Read what the boy asked her and choose the correct options in the reported questions. Then match them with Katy's answers a–f.

Yesterday the boy said:

1 Do you come here often?
2 Can I buy you a coffee?
3 What is your name?
4 Have you got a boyfriend?
5 Where did you meet him?
6 What is he like?

Today Katy is telling her friend:

1 He asked me *did I go there / if I went there* often.
2 He asked whether he *can / could* buy me a coffee.
3 He asked me what *my name was / was my name*.
4 He asked me *did I have a boyfriend / if I had a boyfriend*.
5 He asked me where *I had met / did I meet* him.
6 He asked me *what was my boyfriend like / what my boyfriend was like*.

a I said I had met my boyfriend at a friend's party. ☐
b I told him it was Katy. ☐
c I said he could buy me a coffee and also a cookie if he liked. ☐
d I told him my boyfriend was fantastic and I loved him. ☐
e I said I had a boyfriend, so he was wasting his time. ☐
f I said I went there most lunchtimes. [1]

3 ★★ Look at Rosie's list and complete her conversation with her friend Poppy.

Horrible things my sister has said to me

Monday	Tuesday	Wednesday
1 Shut up!	3 Grow up.	5 Go away.
2 Don't annoy me.	4 Don't be stupid!	6 Stop writing lists!

P: How are things with your sister, Rosie? Are you still writing your list?
R: Yes, I am. I'll tell you. On Monday she 0 *told me to* shut up and 1 ______ annoy her. On Tuesday she 2 ______ grow up and 3 ______ stupid, and on Wednesday she 4 ______ go away and asked me 5 ______ lists.
P: Oh, Rosie. Poor you.
R: Yeah, she's pretty mean, but then she's got her exams coming up soon, so I have decided to forgive her.

4 ★★★ Complete the reported questions and answers from Exercise 1. Use short forms.

0 Grandma asked Lori *what she was going to wear* to the end-of-term party.
Lori said she *was going to wear* a black dress and high heels.
1 She also asked her ______ to the end-of-term party with.
Lori said she ______ with her friends and boyfriend.
2 Then she asked her ______ a boyfriend.
Lori said she ______ a boyfriend.
3 Next, she asked her ______ him.
Lori said she ______ him the month before.
4 After that, she wanted to know ______ good to her.
Lori said her boyfriend ______ good to her.
5 Finally, she asked ______ meet him.
Lori told her grandma ______ meet him at her birthday party.

SHOW WHAT YOU'VE LEARNT

5 Report the questions and imperatives. Use short forms.

0 'Have you arrived safely?'
Mum called as soon as the plane landed and *asked me if I had arrived safely*.
1 'What was the flight like?'
She ______.
2 'Have you been through passport control yet?'
Then she ______.
3 'Did you remember to collect your luggage?'
She even ______.
4 'Don't forget to change some money.'
Next, she ______.
5 'How are you getting to your aunt and uncle's house?'
Still more questions! She ______
______.
6 'Say hello to everyone from me.'
Finally, she ______.
I'm looking forward to a little time away from home!

/6

7.6 Speaking language practice

Asking for permission • Polite requests

1 Put the words in the correct order to form polite requests.

0 the channel / it / is / I / if / OK / change?
Is it OK if I change the channel?

1 here / mind / you / if / do / I / sit?

______

2 you / if / were / could / we / wondering / we / ask / a question?

______

3 toothbrush / I / can / your / borrow?

______

4 me / you / lend / could / your / bike?

______

5 mind / photograph / take / do / if / you / we / your?

______

2 Choose the correct options to complete the responses to the requests in Exercise 1. Then write *G* for giving permission or *R* for refusing permission.

0 *No problem* / *(I'm sorry)* but I'm watching this programme. [R]
1 *Yes* / *No*, not at all. No one is sitting there. [ ]
2 *Yes, that's fine* / *I'd like to help, but* I'm rather busy at the moment. [ ]
3 Well, OK, I suppose *so* / *not*, although it's a bit disgusting. [ ]
4 *Sure* / *Not at all*, I don't see why not. Do you want to borrow my helmet too? [ ]
5 Yes, *I do, actually* / *go ahead*. I'm afraid I don't like being in photographs. [ ]

REMEMBER THIS

Remember that after requests with *Do you mind if I/we …* you say *no*, meaning 'No, I don't mind,' (i.e. it's OK) to give permission; you say *yes*, meaning 'Yes, I do mind,' (i.e. it's not OK) to refuse permission.

3 Complete the conversations with *Yes, I do* or *No, I don't*.

0 A: Do you mind if we leave early?
B: *No, I don't.* You can leave whenever you want.
1 A: Do you mind if I call you Liz?
B: ______ I'd prefer it if you called me Elizabeth.
2 A: Do you mind if the little ones watch television for a while?
B: ______ We have some children's films they might be interested in.
3 A: Do you mind if we smoke?
B: ______ But please go out onto the balcony and close the door.
4 A: Do you mind if I open the window?
B: ______ You'll let the mosquitoes in if you do.

4 Complete the words in the conversations. Some letters are given.

Conversation 1: Alan and Driver

In a taxi:

A: Excuse me, [0]*is it* OK *if* I eat my sandwich in the taxi?
D: [1]**W**______, OK, I **s**______ so. Actually, it smells very nice. [2]**C**______**d** I have a bite?
A: Er …

Conversation 2: Floyd and Majorie

In the shopping centre car park:

F: Hi, sorry to disturb you, but you look like a very sweet old lady and I [3]**w**______ **w**______ **i**______ I **c**______ ask you to watch my shopping while I go get some change for the parking machine. There are too many bags to carry down those stairs again and if I leave them here, I know someone will steal them.
M: [4]**N**______, **n**______ **a**______ **a**______, young man, you [5]**g**______ **a**______.
F: Really? How kind! You see, even though you are old, you are still useful. Back in two minutes!

Floyd leaves to get change.

M: Useful? Well, how rude!

Marjorie takes out her mobile phone.

M: Dorothy! Bring the car round quickly. We've got some extra free shopping today.

Conversation 3: Duncan and Mum

D: Mum?
M: Yes?
D: [6]**D**______ **y**______ **m**______ **i**______ I borrow your car tonight?
M: [7]**S**______, I **d**______ **s**______ **w**______ **n**______.
D: Really? Fantastic!
M: There's hardly any petrol in it though, so you'll have to fill it up.
D: No problem. Oh … er, Mum?
M: Yes?
D: [8]**C**______**n** I borrow some money?
M: Well, Duncan, I'd like [9]**t**______ **h**______ **b**______ I think I gave you £20 yesterday, didn't I?
D: Oh. Er, yes! Yes, of course you did, sorry. I'll use some of that.

Do you mind if I open the window?

7.7 Writing

A review of an event

1 Complete the puzzle with the following words.

- two adjectives which mean 'very bad' (2, 9)
- one adjective to describe nice tasting food (8)
- one modifier for base adjectives (7)
- one modifier for extreme adjectives (3)
- four adjectives which mean 'very good' (1, 4, 5, 6)

1 b			l	l				t	
2 t				i	b		e		
3 a	b								y
4 a			z			g			
5 f			t	a	s				
6 l		v			y				
7 e	x		r				l	y	
8 d		l		c					
9 a		f							

2 Read the article and put the paragraphs in the correct order (1–5). Then choose the best title.

A ___ B ___ C ___ D ___

1 The village anniversary ☐
2 Last weekend was nice ☐
3 A bright, beautiful and busy 400th birthday ☐

3 Replace the underlined words in the article with more descriptive alternatives from Exercise 1. Use each word only once. Sometimes more than one answer is possible.

Abbeydalevillagenews.com

A Saturday began with an early morning fun run. It was [0]nice Lovely weather and when the sun rose, the sky turned a(n) [1]very ______ pretty orangey-blue colour. When the runners reached the finish next to the abbey, the sun was already high in the sky, the music had started and the smell of [2]nice tasting ______ food was everywhere.

B Unfortunately, the traffic in the village was [3]bad ______. Trying to drive through the village was almost impossible and the sound and smell of the cars was [4]bad ______. Maybe next year one of the farmer's fields outside the village can be used as a car park.

C It is not often you get to say, 'Happy 400th birthday!' but last weekend in our village that's exactly what we did. 400 years ago, a group of monks decided to build an abbey, or church, next to the river and our village grew up around it. The ruins of the abbey are still standing today and that's where the anniversary celebrations were held.

D Except for the traffic, it was a [5]nice ______ day. I think every town and village should have a day when they celebrate their community and its history.

E By midday, everyone from the area was there enjoying the [6]nice ______ sunshine. All around the ruins, there were colourful market stalls and people selling [7]nice ______ local food. There were some great live bands and a(n) [8]really ______ fabulous play which told the story of the village.

SHOW WHAT YOU'VE LEARNT

4 You have seen this announcement on an international students' website.

Reviews wanted: Unusual school events!

Has there been an interesting event at your school recently? Write a review of the event for the website, explaining what happened during the event, whether you enjoyed it and what changes you would suggest for the next time this event is held.

Write your review in 140–190 words.

SHOW THAT YOU'VE CHECKED

In my review of an event:

- I have begun with an interesting, funny or unusual title to attract the reader's attention. ☐
- I have asked a question or giveen interesting facts in the introduction to hold the reader's attention. ☐
- I have described the event using a variety of adjectives and modifiers. ☐
- I have made my descriptions interesting by describing what I saw, heard, smelled and tasted. ☐
- I have finished with a recommendation for the reader. ☐
- I have checked my spelling and punctuation. ☐
- I have written at least 140 words. ☐

7.8 Use of English

Word formation

1 For questions 1–9, read the article below. Use the word given in capitals at the end of some of the lines to form a word that fits in the gap in the same line. There is an example at the beginning.

The history of television

The development of television is a long and [0] *fascinating* story, as interesting as any of today's	FASCINATE
amazing programmes. A new [1] ___________ film tells the story of television's history.	DOCUMENT
Paul Zimmer, the [2] ___________ of the film, explains: 'Most people agree that television has had a	DIRECT
bigger effect on society than any other [3] ___________ in history, particularly on family life. No other	INVENT
form of [4] ___________ has changed people's lives more. I wanted television to tell the story of its	ENTERTAIN
own life, almost like an [5] ___________ , not just as a list of things that happened. So the film shows	BIOGRAPHY
recordings from some of the most [6] ___________ TV programmes ever made to show how TV has	IMAGINE
changed over time.'	
'The really old programmes are my favourites,' says Paul. 'It was a very new technology, so the	
[7] ___________ weren't very good! They often forgot what to say! And because it was a new	PRESENT
technology, there were very few [8] ___________ television broadcasters. They make today's mix of	PROFESSION
soap operas, [9] ___________ shows and sitcoms look absolutely brilliant!'	REAL

Key word transformations

2 For questions 1–6, complete the second sentence so that it has a similar meaning to the first sentence, using the word given. Do not change the word given. You must use between two and five words, including the word given. There is an example.

0 Do you like watching the latest programmes and films?
KEEP
Do you always *keep up with* the latest programmes and films?

1 It's a shame that I don't know how to vlog.
ONLY
If ______________________ to vlog.

2 I don't have enough money, so I can't go to the festival.
IF
I'd go to the festival ______________________ money.

3 Can I show the rest of the class your video?
WONDERING
I ______________________ show your video to the rest of the class.

4 The programme wasn't as good as I expected.
UP
The programme didn't ______________________ expectations.

5 Felix had a hit single ten years after he started playing guitar.
BEEN
Felix ______________________ ten years before he had a hit single.

6 'Don't try and play this music too fast!' the music teacher said to Fiona.
NOT
The music teacher ______________________ the music too fast.

7.9 Self-assessment

1 For each learning objective, tick the box that best matches your ability.

☺☺ = I understand and can help a friend.
☺ = I understand and can do it by myself.
☹ = I understand some, but have some questions.
☹☹ = I do not understand.

			☺☺	☺	☹	☹☹	Need help?
7.1	Vocabulary	I can talk about and give my opinion about TV programmes.					Students' Book pages 84–85 Word Store page 15 Workbook pages 80–81
7.2	Grammar	I can report what other people said.					Students' Book page 86 Workbook page 82
7.3	Listening	I can understand the main points of a short monologue.					Students' Book page 87 Workbook page 83
7.4	Reading	I can find specific detail in an article.					Students' Book pages 88–89 Workbook pages 84–85
7.5	Grammar	I can report questions and imperatives.					Students' Book page 90 Workbook page 86
7.6	Speaking	I can ask for permission and make polite requests.					Students' Book page 91 Workbook page 87
7.7	Writing	I can write a review of an event.					Students' Book pages 92–93 Workbook page 88

2 What can you remember from this unit?

New words I learned (the words you most want to remember from this unit)	**Expressions and phrases I liked** (any expressions or phrases you think sound nice, useful or funny)	**English I heard or read outside class** (e.g. from websites, books, adverts, films, music)

7.10 Self-check

1 Choose the correct options.

0 We are proud to announce that the new judge on *The X Factor viewer / panel / broadcast* is …
1 Some of the scenes in that new Jim Carey comedy are *absolutely / extremely / very* hilarious.
2 Miley Cyrus' new website received 4 million *hits / shares / links* in the first hour it was online.
3 The director tells the actors what to do and the *editor / performer / producer* is responsible for actually getting the film made.
4 Contestants in the new series will *view / compete / audition* for the chance to go into space on a commercial space flight.
5 I thought the final episode was *quite / absolutely / extremely* disappointing. Not terrible, but not as good as the rest of the series.

/5

2 Complete the sentences with words that have a similar meaning to the words in brackets. The first letter of each word is given.

0 It costs a lot to **p**ost (send) a parcel to England. It's cheaper to order online and get free UK delivery.
1 Amy **s**_______ (puts photos, videos, etc. online) videos and photos all day long. I don't think she actually does any studying!
2 Dylan **c**_______ **a**_______ (found) a video on YouTube that was exactly what he needed for his school project.
3 Lucy **c**_______ **u**_______ **w**_______ (thought of) an idea for a charity event.
4 Adam **g**_______ **i**_______ (became interested in) vlogging after reading about it online.
5 The latest edition of *Grand Theft Auto* really **l**_______ **u**_______ **t**_______ (matches) expectations. It's amazing.

/5

3 Complete the sentences with the words in the box. There are two extra words.

auditions edit ~~link~~ post present rehearsal share viral

0 Click on the link to find out more about next week's episode of *Royal*.
1 If you would like to be in the school play, _______ will be held on Friday at 15.30 in the school hall.
2 OK, look into the camera and tell us what happened. Don't worry if you go wrong. We can _______ the film later.
3 Snoop Dogg and Steve Carell will both _______ awards at this year's MTV Movie Awards.
4 Visit our website to find all the latest _______ videos, watched by millions across the web.
5 Today's _______ showed that there is still a lot of work to do before we are ready to put on this play.

/5

4 Find and correct the mistakes in the reported statements.

0 TV presenter: 'Your show is the best I've ever seen.'
The TV presenter ~~said~~ the star that his show was the best he'd ever seen. told
1 Jo: 'I am watching a film, Ann.'
Jo told Ann I was watching a film. _______
2 Kim: 'I haven't seen the film yet.'
Kim told she hadn't seen the film yet. _______
3 Tim: 'I missed the show yesterday.'
Tim said he had missed the show yesterday. _______
4 Mollie: 'We'll meet here at six o'clock.'
Mollie said we'll meet there at six o'clock. _______
5 Ben: 'It can't be the same actor.'
Ben said it can't be the same actor. _______

/5

5 Read the conversation between Phil, the head of a Drama school, and Ruby. Then complete the reported questions and statements.

P: Do you really want to be an actress?
R: Yes, I do.
P: Are you sure?
R: I'm sure.
P: Have you studied Drama?
R: No, I haven't.
P: Can you act?
R: Yes, I can.
P: Show me.

0 He asked me if I really wanted to be an actress.
1 He asked me whether _______ .
2 He asked me if _______ .
3 I replied that _______ .
4 He asked me whether _______ .
5 And then he asked me _______ .

/5

6 Read the text and choose the correct answer, A, B or C.

I took Grandma to buy a new TV last weekend. The shop assistant asked us what kind of TV we [0]__ interested in and Grandma [1]__ she wanted a black and white TV that was square and had at least four channels. The assistant told her [2]__ colour TVs and that they all [3]__ more than four channels. She said she wanted an absolutely [4]__ one to the old one.

In the end, we persuaded her to buy a little colour TV. Altogether, it came [5]__ £79.99, which I thought was good value, but Grandma thought it was 'ridiculous'. Now she loves her little TV and says it was worth every penny. ☺

	A	B	C
0	A were	B are	C have been
1	A told	B said	C said him
2	A they only sold	B they only sell	C we only sell
3	A have had	B had had	C had
4	A same	B identical	C similar
5	A up to	B into	C to

/5

Total /30

8 GOOD CITIZENS

8.1 Vocabulary

Human qualities • Suffixes • Verb phrases

SHOW WHAT YOU KNOW

1 Choose the correct options.

1 Could you really run into a burning building? Do you think you are *courageous / courage* enough to become a fire-fighter?
2 Most people show great *enthusiastic / enthusiasm* during their first few weeks as gym members. Unfortunately, for many people it doesn't last.
3 Be *honest / honesty* with yourself. Do you always treat other people the way you would like them to treat you?
4 I'd like to meet an intelligent and kind girl. *Modest / Modesty* is also important, I feel.
5 Diane is absolutely *determined / determination* to find a job as soon as she leaves school.
6 Jodie's aunt is extremely rich but not very *generous / generosity*. She only gave Jodie £5 on her birthday.
7 A *loyal / loyalty* fan doesn't stop supporting his team just because the team stops winning.
8 Since the new Prime Minister was elected, there has been a sense of *optimistic / optimism* in the country.

WORD STORE 8A
Suffixes – forming nouns

2 Complete the texts with the correct form of the words in brackets.

The Royal Society for the Prevention of [0] Cruelty (cruel) to Animals would like to thank you for your [1] _______ (donate) to our organisation. Your [2] _______ (kind) is very much [3] _______ (appreciate).

Thanks for looking after the cat while we were away. It's nice to have such [4] _______ (help) people living in the [5] _______ (neighbour). Let us know if we can do anything for you.

Choosing the right career
At The Job Centre, we always advise young people to try to find [6] _________ (employ) which [7] _________ (engage) them. Put simply, this means choosing a career that you find interesting rather than one which pays the highest salary.

3 Find and correct the mistakes in six of the sentences.

0 We got you this gift to show our ~~appreciate~~ for all your help this year. appreciation
1 The new sports equipment at our school was paid for with donate from local businesses. _________
2 Congratulations on your engage. We hope you'll be very happy together. _________
3 We employ young people during the school holidays because the theme park gets very busy. _________
4 The lady in the driving school office was useless. Helpful was not one of her qualities. _________
5 McQueen's new film explores the cruel of the slave trade. _________
6 Your stupid has got you into trouble again. I wish you'd behave like an adult for a change. _________
7 Many philosophers agree that friendship is one of the most important elements of happiness. _________
8 My neighbourhood had a barbeque on his balcony and someone called the police. _________

WORD STORE 8B
Suffixes – forming adjectives from nouns and verbs

4 Complete the adjectives in the conversations. The first letters of each adjective are given.

Conversation 1

DJ Dan: Hi, you're through to 101.5 Chorley FM on DJ Dan's phone-in show. Today's topic is celebrities. Hello on line 1! What's your name and what do you want to say?

Dave: Hi, I'm Dave. Personally, I find it hard to be [0] **symp**athetic with celebrities and models who earn millions of pounds for doing very little and at the same time complain how [1] **stress**______ their lives are. I think people like that are partly to blame for the [2] **material**______ and selfish society that we live in nowadays. I mean, they could have real problems and real stress in their lives. They could be [3] **job**______ or even [4] **home**______ and then they'd really know how hard life can be.

DJ Dan: Thanks, Dave. I'm sure a lot of our listeners will be nodding their heads in agreement with that comment. Who have we got on line 2?

Conversation 2

DJ Liv: Hi, you're through to Talk FM's *Late Night Love Line* with me, DJ Liv. Who would you like me to play a song for and why?

Tess: Hi, Liv, this is Tess. I'd like you to play a song for my boyfriend, Colin. It's our two-year anniversary today and he's the best boyfriend in the whole world. He's [5]**sensi**______ , [6]**honour**______ and [7]**rel**______ , and he bought me a very [8]**imagin**______ anniversary present.

DJ Liv: What was that, Tess?

Tess: A hot-air balloon ride.

DJ Liv: Wow! So you are not afraid of heights then?

Tess: Oh no. Colin said he wants to ask me a very important question when we are high up in the sky.

DJ Liv: Oh Tess! Is he going to ask you to marry him, do you think?

Tess: I'm not sure, but I'm [9]**hope**______ .

DJ Liv: And what song would you like me to play for Colin, Tess?

Tess: *I Do, I Do, I Do, I Do, I Do* by Abba, please.

WORD STORE 8C

Verb phrases

5 Complete the advert with the correct form of the verbs in the box. There are two extra verbs.

do give have ~~help~~
make put take warm

Highfield Children's Home
Could you help make a difference?

Highfield Children's Home is looking for teenage volunteers to [0] *help* us out during the summer holidays. Contact with lively, positive young people always [1]__________ a smile on our children's faces and the chance to talk, play and spend time with another young person from outside the home can really [2]__________ their day.

Maggie, a local teen who [3]__________ us a hand last Christmas, had the following to say about her experience:

'I loved every minute I spent at Highfield. The kids were lovely and on my last day they sang a song to say goodbye, which really [4]__________ *my heart. I'd recommend the experience to any young person who wants to* [5]__________ *a good deed and have a lot of fun at the same time.'*

REMEMBER THIS

There are many expressions with the word *hand*. They're worth remembering because they are often used in everyday language.

6 Read the sentences and choose the option that has a similar meaning to the underlined phrases.

1. Could you hand me that bottle of water? *pass / buy*
2. First aiders are on hand to help anyone who injures themselves. *paid / available*
3. You can get some real bargains in second-hand clothes shops in England. *used / small*
4. I'm going to hand out the exam papers now, but please do not open them until I say so. *take in / give out*

SHOW WHAT YOU'VE LEARNT

7 Complete the sentences with the correct form of the words in brackets.

1. I spent hours helping him, but he didn't show any ________ (appreciate). Not even a thank you.
2. I'm looking for whatever ________ (employ) I can get. There aren't many summer jobs for teenagers here.
3. The man was found guilty of ________ (cruel) to animals and fined €5,000.
4. There's nowhere for young people to hang out in our ________ (neighbour), so we just meet in the car park.
5. There's no need to be so ________ (sense). I wasn't criticising you.
6. I will always buy this brand of phone. They are always so ________ (rely).
7. The most important characteristic to look for in a life partner is ________ (kind).
8. Please make a ________ (donate) to our charity event. It really is for a good cause.
9. How did you lose the car keys? I just can't believe your ________ (stupid)!
10. I've known Karen for twenty years – her ________ (friend) is really important to me.

8 Choose the correct answer, A, B or C.

1. If you've made a mistake, the ___ thing is to apologise.
   A honourable B hopeful C imaginative
2. She's just so ___ . All she thinks about is money.
   A jobless B materialistic C sympathetic
3. What great news! You've totally made my ___ !
   A heart B hand C day
4. I try to ___ a good deed every day.
   A do B give C make
5. You story was lovely – it certainly put a ___ on my face!
   A heart B deed C smile
6. You can't carry all those heavy bags, Mrs Ferguson. Shall I give you a ___ ?
   A hand B face C heart

/16

8.2 Grammar

The Passive

SHOW WHAT YOU KNOW

1 Complete the sentences with the correct passive form of the verbs in brackets.

0 YouTube was started (start) by an American, a Taiwanese and a Bangladeshi.
1 YouTube _______ (create) on Valentine's Day 2005.
2 The first video, called *Me at the Zoo*, _______ (not post) until April 2005.
3 Currently, around 100 hours of video _______ (upload) to YouTube every minute.
4 *Gangnam Style* by Psy _______ (watch) by billions of viewers since it was posted.
5 YouTube _______ (buy) by Google in 2006 for US$1.65 billion.
6 A lot of money _______ (make) by people who have started successful YouTube channels.

2 ★ Choose the correct options to make passive sentences.

1 The crown jewels of England *have kept / have been kept* at the Tower of London since 1303.
2 *Will the student meeting be held / Will we hold the student meeting* in the cafeteria?
3 Until recently, prisoners in this jail *weren't being given / weren't giving* basic medical care.
4 Jennifer's dress *didn't design / wasn't designed* by Chanel. It's an Armani.
5 The plants are dying because they *aren't watering / aren't being watered* regularly.
6 *Are the school gates unlocked / Do they unlock the school gates* at eight every morning?

3 ★★ Read Kitty's message and complete the sentences with the correct passive forms.

Hi Henry,

Robin and I have finally organised everything for Nina's leaving party. We're not holding it at Big Mike's Burger Restaurant anymore because they are renovating the place that weekend. ☹

Anyway, we have decided that we will hold it at Pizza Land instead (Nina's dad hasn't paid the deposit yet, but he promised to do it soon). Eatout.com recommends Pizza Land, so it should be OK. I invited James, but unfortunately, he can't make it. Everyone else has said yes, so there will be eleven of us. A mini-bus will pick everyone up from Robin's house at 6 p.m.

C U then, ☺
Kitty xx

0 Everything has been organised by Robin and Kitty.
1 The party _________ at Big Mike's Burger Restaurant.
2 Big Mike's Burger Restaurant _________ that weekend.
3 Instead, the party _________ at Pizza Land.
4 The deposit _________ by Nina's dad yet.
5 Pizza Land _________ by eatout.com.
6 James _________ by Kitty, but he can't make it.
7 Everyone _________ from Robin's house at 6 p.m.

4 ★★★ Rewrite the sentences in the passive. Change the verb form, then add a phrase with *by* + one of the phrases in the box.

the amateur theatre group	~~the factory workers~~
the director and the editor	the Kenyan runner
the nurse	the Physics teacher

0 They produce 100 mobile phones per hour here.
100 mobile phones per hour are produced by the factory workers here.
1 We are performing *Les Miserables* this year.
_________________ _________ this year.
2 She injected me with a steroid.
_________________ with a steroid _________ .
3 They were editing the film at the studio.
_________________ at the studio _________ .
4 He has broken the marathon world record again.
_________________ _________ again.
5 She will give out the exam papers in five minutes.
_________________ _________ in five minutes.

SHOW WHAT YOU'VE LEARNT

5 Complete the notices with the correct passive form of the verbs in brackets.

1 **Tomorrow at 2 p.m. the water _________ (turn off) for half an hour.**
2 The swimming pool _________ (clean) at the moment and will reopen in twenty minutes.
3 My bike _________ (steal) from here last night. Please call 409 709 if you saw or heard anything.
4 RUBBISH _________ (COLLECT) ONCE A WEEK ON A THURSDAY MORNING.
5 **This week's prize _________ (not collect) yet. Please check your ticket and contact us if you are the winner.**
6 The council removed the recycling bins from this location as they _________ (use). Your nearest bins are now at the end of Pope Street.

/6

8.3 Listening language practice

Interview with a young offender • Verb-noun collocations

1 Read the extract from an interview with an ex-offender and choose the correct verb patterns for the verbs in bold a–g.

Extract from Students' Book recording CD•3.39 MP3•128

A: Is it true that some young offenders [a]**like** *be / being* in prison because they have a better life inside than outside?

B: Yeah. That's definitely true. One of my mates was homeless [1]__ he came [2]__ prison. He was worried [3]__ being released – [4]__ prison he got food and clean clothes and a warm cell. Outside, he was living in a box [5]__ the street. The day he was released, he walked [6]__ the prison car park and smashed the windows on five cars in the car park. He was back here [7]__ a few days.

A: Hm, well, that brings me to another point. The government [b]**want** *to improve / improving* conditions in young offenders' prisons. But some people say that this is wrong. They say that these are young people who have committed crimes and they [c]**should** *to be punished / be punished*. One prison guard said, 'They have education, they have a gym and television – it's like a holiday camp!' What do you say to that?

B: But it's not a holiday camp – we can't see our friends or our family. Doors are locked. I don't want to go back there. If you want young people to change, you [d]**can't** *lock / to lock* them in a cell and [e]**expect them** *changing / to change*. You [f]**have to** *educate / educating* them and [g]**make them** *believe / to believe* that there is a better life in front of them. Simple as that.

2 Read the interview again and choose the correct answer, A, B or C, for gaps 1–7.

	A	B	C
1	A after	B before	C during
2	A onto	B by	C into
3	A about	B for	C of
4	A on	B to	C in
5	A by	B on	C along
6	A into	B in	C on
7	A with	B before	C in

3 Listen and check your answers to Exercises 1 and 2.

4 Use the prompts to complete the prisoners' words.

0 (should/be)
You *should be* very careful who you talk to. There are some very dangerous men in here.

1 (not want/leave)
I __________ prison because outside I'll be homeless, jobless and penniless.

2 (not expect/anyone/visit)
Well, I really __________ me now while I'm in here. I never had any friends and my family don't speak to me after what I did.

3 (have to/spend)
Most days, we __________ twenty-two hours in our cells. We only come out for meals and exercise.

4 (make/us/clean)
The prison guards __________ our cells every morning last week.

5 (like/share)
Nobody in here __________ a cell. One of the worst things about prison life is the lack of privacy.

6 (can't /remember)
I've been locked up for so long that I __________ what it feels like to be free.

WORD STORE 8D
Verb-noun collocations

5 Complete each pair of sentences with the correct form of one of the verbs in the box. There are two extra verbs.

~~break~~	commit	make	offer
release	spend	take	

0 a You *broke* the rules of the game, so you have to go back to the beginning.
b My mum says she has never *broken* the law in her life.

1 a The US government is ________ a reward of $1,000,000 for information leading to the arrest of the head of the terrorist organisation.
b Joanne spent so much time at the ice rink that they ________ her a job during the holidays.

2 a An English mass murderer known as The Yorkshire Ripper ________ thirteen murders in five years before he was finally caught.
b Many people don't realise they are ________ a crime when they download music or films illegally.

3 a It is unlikely that this man will ever be ________ from prison. He is simply too dangerous.
b They are ________ my grandad from hospital this week, so we're going to visit next weekend.

4 a I seem to be very good at ________ a fool of myself in front of my girlfriend's parents.
b The judge gave the maximum prison sentence to Mr Barnes in order to ________ an example of him to other potential drunk-drivers.

8.4 Reading

The Shawshank Redemption • Definitions • Collocations with *make*

Glossary

redemption (n) = *formal* saving someone or being saved from evil
theatre company (n) = a group of actors, dancers or singers who work together
require (v) = need
commitment (n) = *uncountable* the hard work and loyalty someone gives to an organisation, activity, etc.

1 Read the article quickly and choose its aim.

1 to describe a film and give an update on its star's current work ☐
2 to describe a film which shows what life is like in modern prisons ☐
3 to describe a film in which prisoners were used as actors ☐

2 Read the article again and choose from the sentences (A–E) the one which fits each gap (1–4). There is one extra sentence.

A Now, more than twenty years later, Robbins is back in prison. ☐
B Since 2008, it has been the number one film on the well-known film review website IMDB (Internet Movie Database). ☐
C This is probably because the film was released at the same time as *Forrest Gump* and *Pulp Fiction*. ☐
D Robbins also described the success of the lessons, which have been taken by more than 300 prisoners. ☐
E It would ruin the film to give any more details of the story here. ☐

Filmfocus.org

A portrait of life inside

According to many viewers and critics, *The Shawshank Redemption* is one of the greatest films ever made. It is a prison-drama adapted from a short story by Stephen King and in the mid-nineties it was nominated for seven Oscars, including Best Actor and Best Picture. Although it is set behind bars, it tells a heartwarming story. It did not make a lot of money when it was first shown in cinemas, but it is now loved by audiences around the world. [1]___ This puts it one place above Francis Ford Coppola's classic mafia movie *The Godfather*.

Set in the 1940s, *The Shawshank Redemption* tells the story of Andy Dufresne, a young and successful banker who is convicted of the murder of his wife and her lover and sentenced to life imprisonment in Shawshank Prison. Over the years, Andy, played by actor Tim Robbins, learns to adapt to life in prison with the help of his friend Red, an older convict, played by Morgan Freeman. [2]___ However, it won't spoil it to say that the plot shows the power of hope, courage and determination, even in situations that seem cruel and hopeless.

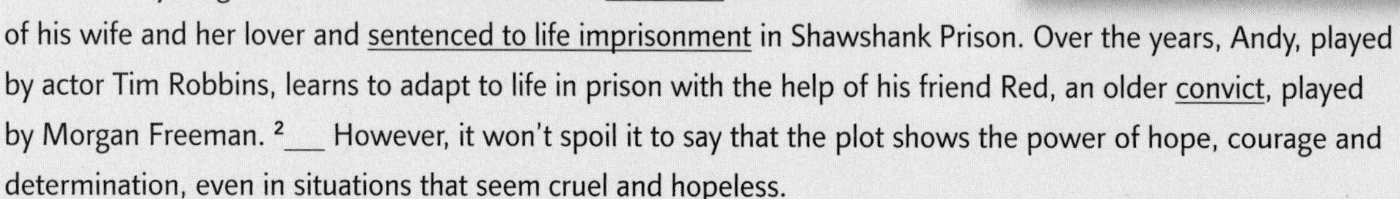

The Shawshank Redemption was filmed in the early nineties, and to prepare for his starring role, Tim Robbins spent time locked up alone in a real prison cell. [3]___ Thankfully, he is not there as an inmate this time, but as a teacher who gives acting lessons to prisoners in a medium-security jail in California. The project has been running for several years with the help of a theatre company called The Actor's Gang, which was started by Robbins in the 1980s. In an interview with CBS news, Robbins explained that the opportunity to act provides prisoners with a break from the prison routine and a chance to explore new emotions and new realities.

When he was asked whether prisons should be offering such enjoyable activities to inmates who have been found guilty of serious crimes, Robbins replied, 'It's not a good time. It's tough work they're doing. It's physically demanding and it requires discipline. We want full commitment from them and it takes a lot of courage.' [4]___ He said that none of the prisoners who completed the programme had reoffended and returned to prison after they were released.

3 Read the article again. Are the statements true (T) or false (F)?

1 According to the article, *The Shawshank Redemption* is the greatest film ever made. ☐
2 *The Shawshank Redemption* was directed by Francis Ford Coppola. ☐
3 In the film, Andy is found guilty of an extremely serious crime. ☐
4 *The Shawshank Redemption* is set in the 1990s. ☐
5 Tim Robbins is a prisoner in a jail in California. ☐
6 Robbins is now helping prisoners learn a new skill. ☐
7 Robbins wants to help prisoners enjoy their time in prison. ☐
8 The lessons have had a positive effect on prisoners after their release. ☐

4 Match the underlined words in the article with their definitions.

0 two informal phrases meaning 'in prison'
inside, *behind bars*
1 two phrases meaning 'prisoner'
__________, __________
2 another word for 'prison' __________
3 found guilty of a crime __________
4 sent to prison for life by a judge
____
5 a small room in which prisoners are locked
____
6 let out of prison __________
7 committed another crime after leaving prison
____

REMEMBER BETTER

In addition to translations of useful words and phrases in your vocabulary notes, try to write simple definitions in English if you can. This will help you increase your range of vocabulary and encourage you to think in English, not your own language.

A Complete the definitions with the words in the box.

allergy	discuss	~~earthquake~~	flowing	group
help	money	plants	river	wall	~~wave~~

0 **tsunami** a giant *wave* caused by an *earthquake* under the sea
1 **panel** a(n) __________ of people who __________ or judge something
2 **dam** a special ________ built across a(n) ________ or stream to stop the water __________
3 **hay fever** a(n) __________ caused by trees and other __________
4 **donate** give something, especially __________, to __________ other people

B Choose other words from the Word Stores in the Students' Book and write definitions in English.

WORD STORE 8E
Collocations with *make*

5 Put the words in the correct order to form sentences.

0 smell / made / cooking / Viola / the / of / bacon / hungry
The smell of bacon cooking made Viola hungry.
1 low-energy light bulbs / makes / company / my / dad's
____
2 easier / to predict / where and when / will strike / makes / it / hurricanes / modern meteorology
____
3 makes / the starting gun / a loud noise / and / begins / the race
____
4 his / the customs officer / bag / open / made / Matthew
____

6 Complete the sentences with the words in the box. There are four extra words.

cough	effort	excuse	~~faster~~	
nervous	pilots	seats	stay	walk

0 The new motorway may not be good for the environment, but it makes the journey to Grandma's house much *faster* .
1 Mr Jenkins made us ________ behind after class until we could manage three minutes without laughing. We were there for half an hour.
2 Emma was late again, so she made a(n) ________ – something about the roads being busy. No one really believed her, but she didn't care very much.
3 This factory is where they make the ________ for seventy-five percent of the world's aeroplanes.
4 Just the thought of the auditions for the school play made Harry ________ .

8.5 Grammar

have something done

SHOW WHAT YOU KNOW

1 Complete the sentences with the correct form of the verbs in the box. There are two extra verbs.

carry ~~cut~~ fix massage pierce redecorate whiten

0 Dean *cut* his own hair. It looked terrible.
1 Gosia ___________ her own teeth. After two weeks she couldn't see any difference.
2 Mike attempted to ___________ his own back. He couldn't reach.
3 Marta wanted to ___________ her own ears. She wasn't brave enough.
4 George tried to ___________ his own computer. He made it worse.

2 ★ Read the sentences about the people in Exercise 1 and choose the correct options. Then complete the gaps with the words in the box. There are two extra words.

body piercer dentist doctor ~~hairdresser~~ masseuse mechanic technician

0 Now, Dean *cuts his hair / has his hair cut* by the *hairdresser* .
1 Next time, Gosia *is going to have her teeth whitened / is whitening her teeth* by the ___________ .
2 Mike *didn't have his back massaged / didn't massage his back* by the ___________ .
3 Why didn't Marta *pierce her ears / have her ears pierced* by the ___________ ?
4 After he failed to do it himself, George *fixed his computer / had his computer fixed* by a ___________ .

3 ★★ Look at the list and complete the sentences with the correct form *have/get something done.*

Paris' beauty list

Every week:
0 hair washed and styled (get)
1 nails painted (get)
Last month:
2 eyebrows shaped (have)
3 legs waxed (get)
Next month:
4 back massaged (have)
Already done this year:
5 tattoo removed (already/have)
6 skin treated (have)
Still to do:
7 teeth whitened (have)

0 Paris *gets her hair washed and styled* every week.
1 Paris ___________ every week.
2 Last month she ___________ .
3 Did she ___________ last month?
4 Next month she ___________ .
5 She ___________ this year.
6 Has she ___________ this year?
7 She ___________ yet this year.

4 ★★★ Complete the the conversation with the correct form of *have something done.*

A: Today in the studio we have teenage author Clara Dickens, whose book *Bringing up my Parents* became a bestseller. Clara, has success changed you?
B: Well, I guess I'm the same person. I have the same friends and go to the same school and still work hard. I mean I [0]*don't have my homework done* (not do/ my homework) for me or anything, but yes, in some ways life is different now.
A: How is it different?
B: Well, I'm not like a big Hollywood celebrity or whatever, I mean I [1]___________ (not have/plastic surgery) or anything, but I'm into fashion and stuff, so since my success, I [2]___________ (make/some nice clothes). Oh, and I also have very big feet, so I used to find it difficult to find shoes that fit, but now I [3]___________ (design and fit/my shoes) especially for me.
A: Are your parents sharing in your success?
B: Well, I couldn't have done it without them, so I wanted to thank them, of course. At the moment, we [4]___________ (redecorate/our house), and Mum is going to the dentist regularly because she [5]___________ (completely redo/her teeth). Dad likes old motorbikes, so he [6]___________ (build/a new garage) for his bikes.
A: Great. So let's talk about your new book …

SHOW WHAT YOU'VE LEARNT

5 Rewrite the sentences using the correct form of *have something done.*

0 We changed the locks after the burglary.
We *had the locks changed* after the burglary.
1 Fiona colours her hair green every year for St Patrick's Day.
Fiona ___________ every year for St Patrick's Day.
2 Isobel is piercing her nose on Friday.
Isobel ___________ on Friday.
3 In the end, Scott didn't tattoo a picture of his mum on his back.
4 In the end, Scott ___________ on his back.
Linda and Beth don't whiten their teeth.
Linda and Beth ___________ .
5 Are your uncle and aunt redecorating their kitchen at the moment?
Are your uncle and aunt ___________ at the moment?
6 Have you repaired your bike yet, Paul?
Have you ___________ yet, Paul?

/6

8.6 Speaking language practice

Opinions: talking about advantages and disadvantages

1 Put the words in A and B in the correct order to make phrases. Then choose the correct phrase to complete the conversations.

0 A thing / my / … isn't / all / at *… isn't my thing at all*
B is … / I / what / mean *What I mean is …*
Mark: I want to lose some weight and get fit.
Molly: Why don't you start running? It's cheap and easy.
Mark: In this cold weather? Are you joking? Running in the winter *A*.

1 A benefit / another / that … / is ______________
B advantage / the / of … / main ______________
John: ___ learning to drive is the independence it gives you.
Sarah: Yes, but lessons and cars are both expensive!

2 A lot / there / drawbacks / too / are / a / of ________
B think … / be / to / I / don't / honest, ____________
Beth: It must be great living in the city centre, so close to all the shops and cafés and stuff.
Anne: Well yes, but I'm sure ___ . For example, it's probably really noisy at night.

2 Complete the words in the conversation. The first letter of each word is given.

A: I've decided I want to [0]**d***o* **s***omething* **t***o* **h***elp* **o***ther* **p***eople*, Leah. The thing is I don't know what I could do. Have you got any ideas?
B: Well, [1]**y**_____ **r**_____ **g**_____ **a**_____ making conversation. Why don't you volunteer to call on an elderly person and chat to them? You've always got something to say.
A: Are you saying I talk too much?
B: Ha ha! You? Talk too much? Of course not. Seriously though, I think you'd be really good at it. [2]**I**_____ **n**_____ patient **e**_____ myself. It wouldn't be my thing. [3]**I**_____ **r**_____ organise a sale to raise money for charity or something.
A: [4]**T**_____ **b**_____ **h**_____, **I t**_____ I'd prefer to do that too. We could do it together. We could cook something and sell it during lunch break at school.
B: Cool. Actually, I talked to Katy and Sally about this yesterday and they [5]**w**_____ **r**_____ **i**_____ the idea too. The four of us could bake some cakes and organise a sale together.

BAKE SALE TODAY!

3 Complete the sentences with the singular or plural form of *advantage, disadvantage, benefit* or *drawback*. In each group of sentences, use each word no more than twice.

1 One *benefit* of being an only child is that you get all your parents' time and attention.
One of the main _______ is that you don't have another young person to play with or talk to at home.
Another _______ is that your parents might be overprotective because they only have one child.
Another _______ though is that you don't have to share a room with your brother or sister.

2 There are _______ to single-sex schools. For example, teenagers are less distracted by the opposite sex while they are at school and tend to study more effectively as a result.
One of the main _______ of single-sex schools is that boys and girls don't learn about their differences and similarities.
Another _______ is that exam results are usually better in single-sex schools.
One _______ is that one of the joys and challenges of being young is interacting with the opposite sex.

4 Put the statements in the correct order.

a There are a lot of advantages to owning a dog. *1*
b There are drawbacks too. ☐
c Another drawback of owning a dog is that vet's bills can be very expensive. ☐
d The main benefit is having company. ☐
e One of the main disadvantages is that someone has to look after it if the owners go away. ☐
f Another advantage is exercise from daily walks. ☐

5 Read the conversation and choose the correct options.

Lena: In my [1]*opinion / meaning*, there are a lot of [2]*drawbacks / benefits* to being a man. For example, one of the main [3]*disadvantages / advantages* is that it is easier for men to get highly-paid jobs.
Joey: I guess so, though in [4]*fact / honest*, I think that is slowly changing, isn't it? [5]*How / What* I mean is there are more well-paid and high-powered women than there used to be.
Lena: Well, yes, but to be [6]*true / honest*, I think there is still a long way to go.
Joey: I'm sure you're right, but it's not all great being a man, you know. There are [7]*drawback / drawbacks* too.
Lena: For example?
Joey: Er … well, we have to shave every morning.
Lena: Oh poor you! It must be awful. And you could cut yourself. How do you cope?
Joey: Are you being sarcastic, Lena?
Lena: Me? Never!

8.7 Writing

An opinion essay

1 Complete the linkers in the phrases. Some letters are given.

0 To **b**egi**n** with, I think it's wrong to suggest …
1 I **w**_____**d** like to **p**_____**t o**_____**t** that not everyone feels the same about …
2 For **i**_____**e**, there are currently several female Prime Ministers who …
3 It **s**_____**s** to me **t**_____**t** we need to change our attitude towards …
4 **L**_____**y**, we must not forget that …
5 In **s**_____**y**, if we are really serious about saving the planet, then …
6 **P**_____**t** another **w**_____**y**, it is not acceptable for children to …
7 **M**_____**r**, such changes would also benefit …

2 Choose the correct options to complete the functions. Then match them with the linkers in Exercise 1.

a *give* / *introduce* body paragraphs 0, ☐
b give personal *examples* / *opinions* ☐, ☐
c give *examples* / *paragraphs* ☐
d add further *support* / *point* ☐
e *emphasise* / *introduce* a point by repeating it ☐
f *introduce* / *repeat* the conclusion ☐

3 Read the essay quickly and decide which question the student has answered.

1 Are women better parents than men? ☐
2 Do children really need both a mother and a father to bring them up? ☐
3 Which of your parents had the biggest influence on you as a child? ☐

4 Read the essay again and replace the words in bold with linkers from Exercise 1. Sometimes more than one answer is possible.

SHOW WHAT YOU'VE LEARNT

5 In your English class you have been talking about parents' responsibility for their children. Now your teacher has asked you to write an essay. Write your essay using all the notes below and give reasons for your point of view.

Should parents be punished for their children's bad behaviour?

Notes

- unfair
- ineffective
- _____ (your own idea)

Write your essay in 140–190 words.

SHOW THAT YOU'VE CHECKED

In my opinion essay:

- I have introduced the topic and clearly stated my point of view in the opening paragraph. ☐
- I have included two or three paragraphs with more detailed personal opinions and supported these with reasons and examples. ☐
- I have included a summary of my main point of view in the concluding paragraph and used different words to the statement in the introduction. ☐
- I have included a final comment which leaves the reader with something to think about. ☐
- I have used a variety of linkers to help the reader to follow my essay. ☐
- I have checked my spelling and punctuation. ☐
- I have written at least 140 words. ☐

Like many people, I was raised by both my parents. **As far as I'm concerned** [0]It seems to me that men and women may influence their children differently, but it is incorrect to suggest that women are better parents than men.

First of all [1]____ , the physical connection between mother and child is often stronger than with the father. However, **in my view** [2]____ , this does not mean she is a better parent. For instance, fathers who hold and bathe their babies also develop strong physical bonds with them. **In addition** [3]____ , many babies are bottle-fed meaning that a father can feed his child just as well as a mother.

Next, I would like to point out that although women often spend more time with young children, this does not necessarily make them better parents. **For example** [4]____ , if the father stayed at home, he could look after the child just as well as his partner.

Finally [5]____ , both parents can be good role models. Girls will probably learn more about being female from their mother, but the opposite is also true. **In other words** [6]____ , boys will probably learn more about being male from their father. In addition, it is important to teach children to be good people, regardless of their gender, and men and women are equally able to do this.

In summary [7]____ , I think men and women are equally good at being parents, and I also believe that the ideal approach for parents and children is for partners to share the responsibility for raising a family.

8.8 Use of English

Multiple-choice cloze

1 For questions 1–8, read the article below and decide which answer (A, B, C or D) best fits each gap. There is an example at the beginning.

Rules

A set of rules that people need to live by has been developed by [0]__ society that has ever existed. But sometimes things just go [1]__ far! Here are some rules, past and present, that [2]__ recently voted as the world's most ridiculous!

In England, you are [3]__ the law if you die in the Houses of Parliament. We are not sure how the police would question the [4]__ if this happened, however!

If you hear a knock on your door in Scotland and the stranger outside needs to use your toilet, you must let them in. [5]__ you let them enter your house, you will be punished!

In the UK [6]__ , it says that the head of any dead whale found anywhere along the British coast automatically belongs to the king. The tail, of course, goes to the queen. Let's hope they have a very good chef!

Finally, if you're travelling in the US state of Ohio, remember that you could receive a heavy [7]__ or even be locked [8]__ if you give alcohol to a fish. You have been warned!

	A	B	C	D
0	A some	B most	C all	D every (circled)
1	A too	B well	C quite	D so
2	A are	B have	C were	D did
3	A beating	B breaking	C crossing	D making
4	A sentence	B judge	C witness	D suspect
5	A until	B unless	C although	D before
6	A constitution	B rules	C police	D authorities
7	A fine	B price	C ticket	D charge
8	A to	B off	C up	D in

Open cloze

2 For questions 1–10, read the article below and think of the word which best fits each gap. There is an example at the beginning.

Graffiti

Love it or hate it, graffiti has become a common sight in most [0] *of* the world's cities. But graffiti is not a modern invention. In reality, it has existed [1]__________ ancient times. There are examples of it on buildings dating from Ancient Egypt, Greece and Rome, but back then, the term *graffiti* [2]__________ used in a different way. The word, [3]__________ is an adaptation of the Italian word *graffiato*, literally means 'scratched'. Historical examples of graffiti [4]__________ drawings and writing scratched on the walls of ancient churches, temples and other buildings in ruined towns and cities all [5]__________ the world.

Nowadays many people now see graffiti as an emerging form of modern art. However, unlike other artists, graffiti artists usually have to hide their identities [6]__________ they paint their art in places where it isn't allowed – on public buildings, underground trains or bridges. In most countries, graffiti is [7]__________ the law. In fact, [8]__________ of the most well-known artists has [9]__________ arrested over twenty times! He has even served a six-month prison [10]__________ for criminal damage. At the same time, his works of art sell for millions of dollars. Funny old world!

8.9 Self-assessment

1 For each learning objective, tick the box that best matches your ability.

☺☺ = I understand and can help a friend.
☺ = I understand and can do it by myself.
☹ = I understand some, but have some questions.
☹☹ = I do not understand.

			☺☺	☺	☹	☹☹	Need help?
8.1	Vocabulary	I can talk about human qualities and acts of kindness.					Students' Book pages 96–97 Word Store page 17 Workbook pages 92–93
8.2	Grammar	I can understand and use the Passive.					Students' Book page 98 Workbook page 94
8.3	Listening	I can identify specific detail in an interview.					Students' Book page 99 Workbook page 95
8.4	Reading	I can understand the structure of a text.					Students' Book pages 100–101 Workbook pages 96–97
8.5	Grammar	I can understand and use the structure have something done.					Students' Book page 102 Workbook page 98
8.6	Speaking	I can give my opinion and identify advantages and disadvantages.					Students' Book page 103 Workbook page 99
8.7	Writing	I can present and support my personal point of view.					Students' Book pages 104–105 Workbook page 100

2 What can you remember from this unit?

New words I learned (the words you most want to remember from this unit)	**Expressions and phrases I liked** (any expressions or phrases you think sound nice, useful or funny)	**English I heard or read outside class** (e.g. from websites, books, adverts, films, music)

8.10 Self-check

1 Choose the correct options.

0 The owner of that factory made a big *prize* / (*donation*) / *present* to our school to help build a swimming pool.
1 Without Bella's *friendship* / *engagement* / *appreciation*, I'd be very lonely.
2 Why are you so *negative* / *stupid* / *materialistic*? Possessions are not important compared to love.
3 The news that the school would be closed put a *laugh* / *smile* / *happiness* on the students' faces.
4 He was released from *hospital* / *prison* / *university* after serving twenty years for murder.
5 I don't want to work in the service industry. I want to work for a company that actually makes a *noise* / *point* / *product* of some sort.

/5

2 Choose the correct answer, A, B or C.

0 I don't believe that you have never __ the law. Not even driving too fast or downloading something illegally?
(A broken) B committed C released
1 The missing boy's father __ a reward for any information about his son.
A gave B asked C offered
2 Can you give me a __ with the cleaning? The guests will be here in an hour.
A give B help C hand
3 The story of how the twin sisters eventually met again after all those years really warmed my __ .
A panic B heart C bottom
4 The fact that Charlotte remembered my birthday and gave me a call really __ my day.
A made B gave C did
5 It was really __ of you to lend me your dress. Here's a little gift to say 'thank you'.
A sort B type C kind

/5

3 Complete the sentences with the words in the box.

appreciate cruel hopeful neighbourhood ~~sensitive~~ stupidity

0 Phillip is a very *sensitive* young man. Soap operas make him cry.
1 We _______ your help with the charity event. You've raised a lot of money.
2 This is not a(n) _______ I would like to live in. It's dirty, noisy and dangerous at night.
3 Why would anyone be so _______ to an innocent animal? I just can't understand it.
4 We don't think there's much chance of our community centre staying open, but we remain _______ .
5 I couldn't believe my own _______ . I set my alarm for 7 p.m. instead of 7 a.m. and missed the exam.

/5

4 Complete the sentences with the correct passive form of the verbs in the box. There are two extra verbs.

burgle ~~find~~ finish hunt miss renovate think wash

0 Painite is one of the rarest minerals on Earth. It *is found* in Myanmar in South-East Asia.
1 The dodo, a large flightless bird, _______ until it disappeared completely in the seventeenth century.
2 Fiona's house _______ twice this year, poor thing.
3 The old school sports hall _______ at the moment, so all our PE lessons are held on the field.
4 Our car _______ when the accident happened. The handbrake failed and it rolled into the wall.
5 We're here to say goodbye to Mr Figg, who is retiring today. Mr Figg, you _______ by all your students.

/5

5 Complete the sentences using the prompts and the correct form of *have something done*.

0 (suit/dry-clean)
Charlie *had his suit dry-cleaned* before the wedding.
1 (her phone/fix)
Emma _______ twice this month and today she's having problems with it again.
2 (his health/check)
Our dog _______ by the vet later today.
3 (her legs/wax)
Leona _______ only _______ once in her life.
4 (you/your phone/take away)
_______ ever _______ by the teacher?
5 (Helen/her tattoo/do)
_______ by a professional? I can't tell what it says.

/5

6 Read the text and choose the correct answer, A, B or C.

School Charity Day is coming up next month. Anyone can give a(n) [0]__ , but maybe you can think of something more [1]__ . Who can forget last year's big event, when the head teacher [2]__ by the school nurse? Or when Year 7 got together and [3]__ a good deed by cleaning cars in the local village? They raised over £200 for the animal rescue centre. This year all the money raised [4]__ to the local orphanage. They are planning to [5]__ their children happy by using the money to help build a new playground. So, get thinking.

	A	B	C
0	A reward	(B donation)	C offer
1	A imagine	B imaginative	C imagination
2	A shaved his hair off	B was having his hair shaved off	C had his hair shaved off
3	A did	B made	C had
4	A will give	B will be giving	C will be given
5	A make	B show	C give

/5

Total /30

Focus provides practice of the exam tasks found in upper secondary school leaving exams, as well as international exams like PET, Camridge English: First (FCE), Trinity and PTE (Pearson Test of English). It includes exercises which will help you prepare for all parts of a typical exam – Listening, Reading, Grammar/Use of English, Speaking and Writing. In addition, in this section you will find some useful tips to help you confidently approach different types of exam tasks.

Listening

General guidelines

Do

- Before listening to a recording, read the instructions and questions in the task carefully. Try to predict what kind of information you're going to hear (e.g. how many speakers there could be, what words/expressions they might use).
- When listening for the first time, look at the questions in the task again and note down your answers.
- Before listening to the recording the second time, read all the questions again, especially those you didn't answer the first time. Note down your new answers and check your answers from the first listening.

Don't

- Don't worry if you don't understand some words. You don't need to understand all of the recording to do the task.
- If you don't understand part of the text at first, don't give up! Remember: there will be another chance to listen and your understanding of other parts of the recording will help you the second time.
- Don't spend too much time on the questions which you don't know how to answer. You'll be able to come back to them later. Move on to the next question.
- Don't leave any questions unanswered. If you are not sure, guess!

Multiple choice tasks

- Remember that the questions in the task are usually given in the same order as the information in the recording.
- When listening to the recording for the first time, note down your own answers to the questions. Then compare them to the options provided in the task and choose the ones which are closest in meaning to yours.
- Be careful of the answers which sound very similar to the information in the recording. They are often wrong. Pay attention to synonyms and antonyms.
- Sometimes the information needed to answer the question is not presented directly in the recording – you need to work it out based on what you've heard. If you're not sure which option to choose, use the method of elimination: start by crossing out the answers which are definitely wrong, then those which you think are probably wrong, until you are left with only one option.
- Sometimes when you're answering a question or questions about a conversation, you need to remember to listen for the right speaker. The other options may be mentioned, but not by the person you are asked about.

Sentence completion

- You may need to listen for information to complete some sentences. Usually this will require a maximum of a couple of words. You will definitely hear the words that you need to write in the recording, but the rest of the sentence on your exam sheet will not be identical. It will be rephrased.
- If you need to write a common word, you will be expected to spell it correctly.
- Read all the sentences carefully before you hear the recording for the first time so that you have an idea of what the recording is about. This helps when you are trying to identify the section that has the information you need.
- Try to predict from the sentences what sort of words or information you need to listen for. You might be able to guess that you need to listen for a date, a name, etc.
- Be careful about distraction in the recording. Sometimes if you think you need to listen for a date or year, there could be another date or year mentioned before or afterwards, but it will not fit the context of your sentence.

Matching tasks

- If you need to identify a speaker or place in the task, listen for typical expressions related to people or places. Sometimes one characteristic phrase can help you to choose the right answer.
- If your task is to match particular recordings or parts of a recording to topic sentences, try to summarise the main topic of each part yourself, then choose the answer which is most similar.
- Remember that other speakers might mention words or opinions connected to the point or comment you are looking for, but it will not be exactly right. Don't be distracted or misled.
- Sometimes it can help to listen to the recordings BEFORE you read through the options. Then you have an idea of what the speaker is saying without confusion or preconceptions. Think about the strategy that works best for you.

Reading

General guidelines

Do

- Before you start reading the text, read the instructions for the task carefully. The task will affect the way you read the text.
- Try to identify the kind of text which is used in the task. This can help you predict what sort of information to expect.
- Use the hints in the text to help you understand the context. The title and any photos or other visuals will help you identify the main topic, and the first sentences of paragraphs often summarise their content.
- Read the text quickly to check if your predictions about its content were right. This will also help you later, to identify the parts of the text where the answers are.
- Underline parts of the text which contain language relevant to the questions (single words, phrases, sentences, paragraphs).

Don't

- Don't try to understand every word in a text. You don't need to know every single word to do the task. You can try to guess the meaning of unknown words using different techniques (e.g. guessing from the context or the grammatical form, noticing similarities to words in your own language).
- Don't leave any questions unanswered. If you are not sure, guess!
- Don't spend too much time on any one particular task. Remember that time in the exam is limited and you should try to do all of the tasks.

Multiple-choice tasks

- Identify parts of the text which the questions refer to. Remember that these could differ in length (between one word/phrase and a whole paragraph).
- Focus on the detail of a paragraph or sentence. An incorrect answer might only differ from the correct one in a detail such as the verb tense used or information given that only partly matches the text.
- Remember the words in the correct option will not be the same as those in the text. There will be synonyms and rephrasing.
- Don't be distracted by options that use similar wording. Only one option will be exactly what you need.
- Eliminate the answers which you feel sure are wrong, then make your final choice.

Matching tasks

- One type of matching task requires candidates to match missing sentences with gaps in a text. Remember that this type of task includes an extra sentence or option, so you will have to eliminate unnecessary items.
- When you match missing sentences with gaps in the text, skim the text first, ignoring the gaps, to get its general meaning. Then try to choose the missing information to complete the text, paying special attention to the words that come before and after the gaps.
- It can be useful to look at reference words in the missing sentence and those sentences before and after the gap. A pronoun in the option may refer back to a person in the previous sentence.
- Another type of matching task requires you to match items of information with the sections of a text in which they can be found. It is important to be able to scan the texts quickly to find the matching information.
- Remember that the information will be rephrased in the items, so don't look for the exact words.

Grammar/Use of English

General guidelines

Do

- Before you start reading the text, read the instructions carefully. The task will affect the way you read the text.
- When a text has a title, read it carefully as this can help you predict the main idea of the text.
- Where there are gaps in the text, read it through completely without worrying about the gaps to get the general idea.
- There will be an example for each task. Look at it carefully; it will help you understand what you need to do.

Don't

- Don't try to understand every word in a text. You don't need to know every single word to do the task. You can try to guess the meaning of unknown words using different techniques (e.g. guessing from the context or the grammatical form, noticing similarities to words in your language).
- Don't leave any questions unanswered. If you are not sure, guess!
- Don't spend too much time on any one particular task. Remember that time in the exam is limited and you should try to do all of the tasks.

Multiple-choice cloze

- Read the text first to have an idea what each of its parts is about. Try to understand as much as you can while ignoring the gaps.
- Different types of words are tested in this exam task. For example, you may need to complete a phrasal verb, choose a correct linker or choose between words with similar meanings.
- Read the gap-fill options carefully before deciding which one to choose.
- When deciding which option to use to complete a gap, look at the words before and after the gap. They will give you clues about which option is correct (e.g. look for linkers, personal and object pronouns, adjectives and adverbs).
- Remember that the option you choose must fit grammatically into the sentence and must also have the correct meaning.
- When you've finished, always reread the text to see that it follows logically.

Open cloze

- Read the text first to have an idea what each of its parts is about. Try to understand as much as you can while ignoring the gaps.
- Different types of words are tested in this exam task. For example, you may need to complete a phrasal verb or find a correct linker, article, auxiliary verb, etc.
- When deciding which word to use to complete a gap, look at the words before and after the gap. They will give you clues about what sort of word you are looking for.
- Remember that the word you choose must fit grammatically into the sentence and must also have the correct meaning.
- When you've finished, always reread the text to see that it follows logically.

Word formation

- Read the text first to have an idea what each of its parts is about. Try to understand as much as you can while ignoring the gaps.
- You need to think carefully about how to change the word so that it fits grammatically into the sentence – is it an adjective, an adverb, etc.? You should also consider the meaning – for example, do you need a negative or positive meaning?
- Remember that as well as adding prefixes and suffixes to a word, you may also need to make other changes.
- When you've finished, always reread the text to see that it follows logically.

Key word transformations

- Make sure you read the first sentences carefully and understand the meaning. The second sentence must be as close to that meaning as possible.
- Read the parts of the second sentence which you have to complete carefully too, as parts of it will affect how you complete it. Look for any tense changes or whether you need a singular or plural verb, a negative or a question form, etc.
- Remember that there is a word limit. Always check your number of words as if you have too many, it may mean that you've gone wrong somewhere. A contraction (e.g. don't) counts as two words, not one.

Writing

General guidelines

In a typical exam at this level, you will be asked to write one or two short pieces of written English. Exam tasks include writing an article, a story, a review, a report, an essay, an informal letter or email. There is usually a word limit of between 140 and 190 words.

When writing any of the above mentioned texts, you will need to recognise the function of the type of text you have been asked to write and use appropriate and relevant key language in it. To help you do this, we have provided a reference section in this Workbook (FUNCTION PHRASE BANK, pages 107–111).

Do

- Analyse carefully what kind of writing task it is. Note down in bullet points the most characteristic features of the text type required in the task before you start writing.
- Read carefully all the information that needs to be included in your writing. Also, write down useful words, phrases or grammatical structures that might be relevant to the information.
- Write a plan detailing the information you want to include in each paragraph. If you have time, write some key sentences too.
- Check that you have included all the information required in your writing. Remember to use linkers so that your writing is coherent and easy to follow.
- Check the style of your writing and make sure it's appropriate to the task (e.g. have you used formal or informal language as required?).
- Check that you have an introduction, a main body and a conclusion in your writing, that your paragraphs are clearly defined and that you have written an appropriate number of words.
- Finally, check your grammar and spelling.

Don't

- Don't go over the word limit. It's better to estimate the number of words while you are writing, then shorten or extend your text, than to cross out half of the text when it's already finished. Think about the number of words you need for each paragraph when you write your plan.
- Try not to repeat the same information. By doing this you will waste time and a lot of words from the word count for the piece.
- Try not to use the same words and phrases more than once. Use a range of vocabulary and grammatical structures.
- Do not use incomplete sentences like notes. To write a coherent text, you need to use full sentences and include linkers and subordinate clauses.

Speaking

General guidelines

When preparing for the oral part of an exam, you will need to understand the function of the conversation you are being asked to take part in. The FUNCTION PHRASE BANK (pages 112–113), the VOCABULARY BANK (pages 114–126) and the related PRACTICE EXERCISES (pages 127–134) will help you prepare systematically for spoken interaction tasks.

Do

- Listen carefully to the examiner's questions. Often the questions will be written on your exam sheet.
- Try to stick to the aim of the task. Always keep the question in mind when answering.
- When you are not sure whether you have understood what the examiner has said, ask them to repeat the question.
- If you need more time to decide what to say, ask the examiner to repeat the question and then repeat or paraphrase it, then use 'filler' phrases giving you time to think (e.g. *Let me think ..., It's difficult to say ...*).
- Remember that the examiner has a time limit for each part of the test. If he/she stops you while you're speaking, it's because you have spoken for longer than necessary.
- Try to keep speaking rather than finish your one minute talk or discussion early. It is better to be interrupted because you're talking too much than to say too little.
- When you are asked to discuss something with your partner, make sure you interact by asking for his/her opinion. Don't take it in turns to give your ideas. It should be a real conversation.

Don't

- Try not to repeat the same phrases over and over. Show that you can use a range of vocabulary and grammatical structures.
- Don't ask the examiner to explain something. He/She can only repeat an instruction.
- If you cannot remember a word, don't panic! Try to use strategies that will help you communicate what you want to say (e.g. use a word with a similar meaning or describe the notion or idea you are trying to communicate).
- Don't try to learn whole sentences or detailed answers to things you think you might be asked about. Speak and respond as naturally as possible.
- Make sure you keep in mind that your partner needs to speak as well! Try not to speak too much so that you dominate the conversation or speak too little so that you don't give the examiner enough language to assess.

Accepting suggestions

That sounds fantastic!
I'd love to go.
Well, it's worth a try.
I suppose it'll work.

Agreeing

I (completely) agree that/with ...
I couldn't agree more that/with ...
That's fine with me.
I think so too.
It is true that ...
I am of the same/a similar opinion because ...

Apologising

Informal phrases

I'm really sorry (that) ...
Sorry for bothering you.
Sorry to bother you.
Sorry for any trouble.
Sorry I didn't write earlier, but I ...
Sorry I haven't written for so long./Sorry for not writing for so long.
I'm writing to tell you how sorry I am to/about ...
It will never happen again.

Formal phrases

I apologise for ...
Please accept my apology for ...

Asking for information

Could you tell me when the course starts?
Can you tell me how much it costs?
Could you tell me if there are any discounts?
I would like to know/ask if ...
I would like to know more details about ...
I would like to ask for further information about/concerning ...
I would be (very) grateful if you could ...
I wonder if you could ...
I would like to ask if/when/where/why ...

Closing formulas: emails and letters

Informal phrases

Best wishes,
Bye for now,
See you!
Love,
Take care!
All the best,

Neutral phrases

Yours sincerely,
Regards,

Formal phrases

(Dear Sir or Madam/Editor) Yours faithfully,

Declining suggestions

It doesn't sound very good.
I don't think I fancy it.
I'm sorry, but I can't join you.
I'm not really into ...
I've got some doubts about it.
I don't see how it could work.
Actually, I would prefer not to.

Describing an event

I'll never forget ...
It was an unforgettable (day/occasion/event).
The celebration takes/took place on/in ...
The event is celebrated annually.
The festival originated ...

Describing lost property

I lost (my bag/passport/coat/dog).
I keep (all my files there).
It was something I borrowed/got as a birthday present.
It is of great value./It's a really precious thing.
It means a lot to me.

Describing possessions

It is/was ...
Size: huge/tiny/35cm x 25cm/big
Shape: round/rectangular/square/narrow
Colour: white/red and brown/light/dark green
Material: made of leather/plastic/linen
Age: new/young/old/six years old/modern/ancient
It has/had (two handles/a leather strap/a blue cover/two pockets/short sleeves/a black tail).

Describing a person

The first thing you notice about (him/her) is ...
(He/She) is special for a number of reasons.
(He/She) is the kind of person who ...
The most unusual/interesting person I've ever met is ...
(He/She) dresses casually/smartly/well/in black/fashionably.
(He/She) always wears scruffy/stylish clothes.
Height: of medium height/tall/fairly short/long-legged
Build: muscular/well-built/overweight/skinny/slim/thin
Age: in his teens/middle-aged/in her late forties/elderly
Facial features: round/oval/freckles/dimples/scar/mole/wrinkled/almond-shaped eyes/pale/tanned/a crooked nose/moustache/beard
Hair: balding/short/shoulder-length/long/wavy/curly/thick

Describing a place

The most fascinating/interesting/lively part of the city is ...
The most famous attraction is ...
The town is well-known for its ...
It is the kind of place that/where ...
The place I like best is ...
It is situated in a quiet residential area.
The place is surrounded by ...
It lies in the north/south/east/west of Spain.
It's the most thrilling/picturesque/fabulous place.
The sights are worth seeing.

Disagreeing

I disagree that/with .../I don't agree that/with ...
I am totally against ...
I'm afraid I can't agree with ...
I'm not convinced about ...
I don't think it's the best solution ...
I must say I do not agree/strongly disagree with ...
I am of a different/the opposite opinion because ...
Contrary to popular belief, ...

Encouraging people

Come on, don't be afraid/it's not difficult/it's easy!
Why don't you come and meet interesting people/see great things?
Come and tell us what you think.
Come and have fun!

Ending an email/a letter

Informal phrases

It was good to hear from you.
Email me soon.
I'd better get going./I must go now./Got to go now./I must be going now...
Bye for now.
Looking forward to your news/to hearing from you again.
Say hello to ....
Give me love/my regards to (everyone at home).
Have a nice (trip).
See you (soon/in the summer).
Write soon.
Keep in touch!

Neutral phrases

I look forward to hearing from you/your reply.
I hope to hear from you soon.

Formal phrases

I wonder what other readers think about ...
I hope you will publish more articles about this problem.
I would be grateful if you could publish my email/letter.

Expressing contrast

However, many people say that action should be taken straight away.
Even though/Although many residents support the mayor and his policy, he also has many enemies.
In spite of/Despite winning in the local election, his real ambition was to work for one of the EU institutions.

Expressing doubt

I have read the advert/about your services and/but I am not quite sure if ...
I cannot understand if ...
It is not clear to me if ...

Expressing interest

I am interested in/I have been looking for ...
I am planning to ... and that is why I found this advertisement/offer/text interesting/important.
I would like to thank you for/congratulate you on ...
I was very interested in your (article/editorial/presentation).
I was surprised/fascinated/shocked to ...

Expressing opinion

I (really) believe/think/feel (that) ...
In my opinion/view, ...
The way I see it, ...
It seems/appears to me (that) ...
To my mind, ...
My opinion is that ...
As far as I am concerned,
It can be argued that ...

Expressing preferences

I really enjoy/like/love ... because ...
I prefer ... to ...
I'd like to/I hope to ...
... is great because ...
I find ... boring/dull.
I don't like/I can't stand/I really hate ...
It's not really my thing.

Expressing purpose/result/reason

He worked as a volunteer in the Phillippines to/in order to help local people organise their life anew after the tsunami.
The man committed the crime and therefore/consequently was sentenced to life imprisonment.
The team missed their deadline because of/as a result of numerous mistakes they had made right at the start.

FUNCTION PHRASE BANK, WRITING

Getting in touch with people

Ways to contact people

If you have any information, please contact/call/leave a message for Alison on (0961224466).
If you are interested in ..., call (John/Ms White) on (0961224466).
To join us, call ...
If you have seen it, please ...
Call me/us on ... for more details.

Maintaining contact

Drop me a line sometime.
I hope to hear from you soon.
Give me a call later.
Let me know if you can make it or not.
I was glad to hear about ...
Let me know as soon as possible.

Giving advice

You should/ought to ...
You'd better ...
If I were you, I would ...
It might be a good idea (for you) to ...
Why don't you ... ?
Have you thought of/about ... ?

Giving examples

for example/for instance
like/such as
especially/in particular/particularly

Giving reasons for opinions

I think so because ...
In fact,/Actually, ...
The reason why I believe so is ...

Introducing points in a 'for and against' essay

What are the arguments for and against this idea?
What are the benefits and drawbacks of such a step?
This approach has both advantages and disadvantages.

Inviting

I'd like to invite you to ...
I'd like you to come ...
Would you come to ... ?
I'm writing to invite you to (Warsaw/my party).
I'm having (a party).
I hope you'll be able to join us/to make it.
If you want, you can bring a friend.
You are welcome to ...
Join us today!
Come and meet me ...
Why don't you come ... ?

Listing arguments

First argument

First of all, ...
First/Firstly, ...
To begin with, ...
One (dis)advantage is that ...
The main/major argument in support of ... is that ...
On the one hand/On the other hand, ...
One argument in favour is that ...

Successive arguments

Secondly, ...
Thirdly, ...
Another (dis)advantage is that ...
It is also important/vital to consider ...
In addition/Additionally, ...
Apart from this/that, ...
Moreover/What is more,

Last argument

Finally, ...
Last but not least, ...

Making recommendations

Positive opinion

You'll love it!
I recommend it to everyone.
If you like modern art, you should definitely see it.
It's a must.
I think it's worth seeing because ...
I was impressed by ...
I couldn't put it down.
It's a classic./It's a masterpiece of its kind.
The plot is believable/entertaining/thought-provoking.
It will change the way you see ...
If I were you, I wouldn't hesitate to take part in ...
I highly recommend (joining) ...

Negative opinion

One weakness (of the book/film/workshops) is that ...
It is rather long/boring/confusing/slow.
The cast is awful/unconvincing.
The script is dull.
It is poorly/badly written.

Adjectives

Positive: brilliant/spectacular/striking/impressive/powerful/convincing
Negative: violent/predictable/unconvincing/far-fetched/dull/bland/disappointing
Neutral: slow/sentimental/serious

FUNCTION PHRASE BANK, WRITING

Making requests

Informal phrases

Can you ..., please?/Could you ... ?
Do you think you could ... ?
Let me know if you can ...
Could you tell me ... ?

Formal phrases

Would it be possible for you to ... ?
I would be grateful if you could ...
I wonder if I could ask you to/for ...
I am writing to ask for your help/advice ...

Making suggestions

I think I/you/we should (go to) ...
Perhaps I/you/we could (go to) ...
What do you think about (going to) ...?
What/How about (going to) ... ?
How do you feel about (going to) ... ?
Would you like me to ... ?
Why don't we (go to) ... ?
Let's (go to) ...
Shall we (go to) ... ?
Do you fancy (going to) ... ?

Narrating a story

It all happened some time ago.
It was three years ago.
While I (was playing), ...
First, ...
Then, ...
Suddenly, ...
Unfortunately, ...
Fortunately, ...
It was the best/worst time ever.
We had a great/awful time when we were ...

Opening formulas: emails and letters

Informal phrases

Dear Margaret,
Hi Anne,

Neutral phrases

Dear Mr and Mrs Edwards,
Dear Ms Brennon,

Formal phrases

Dear Sir or Madam,
Dear Editor,

Starting an email/letter

Informal phrases

It was good to hear from you.
I hope you're doing well/you're fine/you're OK.
How are you (doing)?
I'm writing to tell you ...
Thanks for your email/letter.
I wonder if you remember/have heard ...
I wanted to tell you about ...
I just wanted to ask/remind/thank you ...
Just a quick email to tell you ...

Formal phrases

I am writing to thank you for ...
I would like to express my ...
I am writing in connection with (the article/report/editorial) ...
I have just read (the article) entitled ... in Saturday's paper/ this month's edition of ...
I am writing to ask/enquire about ...
I read/found your advertisement in ... and would like to ...

Suggesting solutions

Steps must/should be taken to solve the problem of ...
One (possible) way to solve/overcome this problem is to ...
An alternative solution to this issue is ...

Summing up

All in all/On balance/On the whole/To sum up/In conclusion, ...
All things considered/Taking everything into account, ...

Thanking someone

Informal phrases

I'm writing to thank you for ...
Thank you so much.
It was so/really/very kind of you to ...

Formal phrases

I really appreciate your help.
Thank you for sending it back to me.
I am really grateful for your help.
It was very kind of you.
I hope it is not too much trouble for you.
Thank you for doing me a favour.

Writing about films/books

Introduction

The film/book tells the story of …
The film/story is set in …
The book/novel was written by …
The film is directed by …
It is a comedy/horror film/love story.
This well-written/informative/fascinating book …
It is based on real events/a true story/a book.
It has been made into a film.

Plot description

The story concerns/begins/is about …
The plot is (rather) boring/thrilling.
The plot has an unexpected twist.
The plot focuses on …
The film reaches a dramatic climax …

Writing about future plans

I might …
It is my dream to …
My ambition/goal is to …
I hope that/to …
I am thinking of …

Accepting advice

Good idea!
Good thinking!
That's really helpful.
Oh, I didn't think of that!

Agreeing

I agree.
That's true.
Absolutely!

Asking for advice

Can you do me a (big) favour?
Can you give me some advice?
Do you think I need … ?
What do you think I should (do)?

Asking for an opinion

What do you think about … ?

Asking for information

Could you tell me what the soup is?
Can you tell me what the Mario Special Salad is?
Do you know what the pasta sauce is?
I'd like to know if there are onions in it.

Asking for permission

Can/Could I/we … ?
Is it OK if I/we … ?
We were wondering if I/we could …
Do you mind if I/we … ?

Comparing and contrasting pictures

The three pictures show/focus on/illustrate …
Picture X is/looks interesting/attractive, but …
Picture X is more … than the other pictures.
Picture X isn't as … as the other pictures.

Describing pictures

The picture shows …
In this picture I can see/there is/there are …
in the background/in the middle/in the foreground
on the left/on the right/in front of/behind/next to

Describing physical symptoms

I've got a pain in my chest/back/leg.
I've got a headache/a stomachache/a sore throat/
a temperature/a cough/a runny nose/a rash.
I feel ill/dizzy/sick/very weak.
My stomach/arm/neck hurts.
My ankle/thumb/toe is swollen.

Disagreeing

That's not true.
I'm sorry, I don't agree with you.
I'm not so sure about that.
I'm not convinced.

Disagreeing strongly

No way! (informal)
Are you kidding? (informal)
I'm afraid I completely disagree. (more polite)

Examining/Giving a diagnosis

When did the pain start?
I'm going to examine you.
I'm going to take your temperature.
I'm going to do a blood test.
Breathe in and out.
Open wide.
Lie down, please.
I think you've got indigestion/flu/an infection/a virus.
You're probably allergic to …
If I push here, does it hurt?

Expressing uncertainty

It's hard to say/make out what …, but …
I'm not sure …, but …

Giving advice

The first thing you should do is …
If I were you, I would/wouldn't …
I (don't) think you should …
You (don't) need to …
You (really) ought to …
You must/mustn't …
The best thing would be to …
It's a good idea to …
Why don't you … ?

Giving an opinion

I (don't) think …
I prefer …
In my opinion, …
Personally, …
What I mean is …
In fact, …
If you ask me, …
The thing is …
To be honest, …

Giving permission

Well, OK, I suppose so.
Yes that's fine. No problem.
Sure, I don't see why not.
No, not at all, go ahead.

Justifying your choice

I think the best option would be … because …
I prefer/I'd go for/I'd (definitely) choose … because …
I like … best for two reasons. Firstly, because … and secondly, because …
Out of these three (pictures), I'd choose … because …

Ordering food

Can I order, please?
Do you have any vegetarian dishes?
Can I have chips with that?
Could I have the bill, please?

Recommending treatment

You should eat more slowly/go on a diet.
You need to drink more water.
I'm going to give you a prescription.
I'm going to make an appointment for you.
Take one tablet after each meal.

Refusing permission

I'm sorry, but …
I'd like to help, but …
I'm afraid …
(Do you mind … ?) Yes, I do, actually.

Rejecting other options

The problem with … is that …
Personally, I wouldn't go for … because …
I don't like … because …
I wouldn't choose … because …
The reason I don't like … is because …

Speculating

He/She/It looks (tired).
He/She/It looks as if/as though/like …
It seems to be/Perhaps it's/Maybe it's …
I imagine they're/They're probably …

Talking about advantages and disadvantages

There are a lot of advantages/disadvantages …
One/Another benefit/drawback is that …
The main advantage/disadvantage of … is that …
There are benefits/drawbacks too.
One of the main advantages/disadvantages of … is that …
Another advantage/disadvantage of … is that …

Talking about your skills and interests

(Cooking) isn't my thing at all.
I'm (really) good at (Maths/swimming).
I'm not (patient) enough.
I'd rather (visit an elderly person).
I'm really into (vintage clothes).

Translate the words and phrases.

People

Personality

adventurous ______
aggressive ______
arrogant ______
bad-tempered ______
boring ______
brave ______
caring ______
charming ______
cheeky ______
childish ______
courage ______
courageous ______
creative ______
cruel ______
cruelty ______
determination ______
determined ______
dynamic ______
easy-going ______
enthusiasm ______
enthusiastic ______
fascinating ______
friendly ______
fussy ______
generosity ______
generous ______
grumpy ______
hard-working ______
helpful ______
helpfulness ______
honest ______
honesty ______
honourable ______
imaginative ______
immature ______
inspiration ______
inspiring ______
kind ______
kindness ______
lazy ______
likeable ______
loyal ______
loyalty ______
materialistic ______
mature ______
mean ______
mischievous ______
modest ______
modesty ______
nervous ______
open to sth ______
optimism ______
optimistic ______
outgoing ______
passion ______
passionate ______
patient ______
polite ______
popular ______
positive ______
positive attitude ______
______
qualities ______
realistic ______
relaxed ______
reliable ______
role model ______
rude ______
selfish ______
sense of humour ______
sensitive ______
shy ______
sophisticated ______
stupid ______
stupidity ______
tolerant ______
unfriendly ______
well-mannered ______

Feelings and emotions

admire ______
amazed ______
be impressed by sth ______
calm down ______
cheer up ______
confident ______
confused ______
devastated ______
embarrassment ______
excited ______
exhausted ______
good/bad mood ______
helpless ______
hopeful ______
impressed ______
jealous ______
laugh your head off ______
lonely ______
make sb happy/sad/angry ______
______
negative thoughts ______
nervous ______
positive thinking ______
proud (of sth) ______
reassure sb ______
stressed ______
sympathetic ______
sympathy ______
uncomfortable ______
unhappy ______
upset (about sth) ______
wear a smile ______
worried ______
worries ______
worry ______

Age

adult ______
childhood ______
elderly ______
grow up ______

in your early/mid/late twenties ______

in your teens ______
middle-aged ______
sb is your age ______
youngster ______
youth ______

Appearance

baldness ______
beard ______
cheek ______
chin ______
dimples ______
do your hair ______
facial features ______
freckles ______
go to the hairdresser's ______
hairstyle ______
have your ears pierced ______
put make-up on ______
resemble sb ______

Clothes and accessories

bangle ______
baseball cap ______
boots ______
bracelet ______
coat ______
cotton ______
designer dress ______
flared jeans ______
fleece ______
flying jacket ______
glasses ______
gloves ______
hat ______
high heels ______
jeans ______
jumper/pullover ______
look ______
mittens ______
scarf ______
shirt ______
shorts ______
silver ring ______
skinny jeans ______
snow boots ______
suit ______
sunglasses ______
sweatpants ______
sweatshirt ______
T-shirt ______
tie ______
tights ______
top ______
trainers ______
trousers ______
waistcoat ______

Adjectives describing appearance and clothes

adorable ______
attractive ______
bald ______
blond ______
blue-/brown-eyed ______
casual ______
cool ______
curly/straight/dark/short/long (hair) ______

cute ______
dark-/fair-/long-/short-haired ______

dark-/lighter-/pale-skinned ______

elegant/smart/formal ______
fashionable ______
fat ______
good-looking ______
gorgeous ______
leather ______
medium height ______
mysterious ______
overweight ______
patterned ______
red-headed ______
scruffy ______
short ______
short-sighted ______
skinny ______
slim ______
striped ______
stylish ______
tall ______
vintage ______
well-built ______
well-dressed ______
woollen ______

Clothes and appearance – verbs and phrases

dress casually/smartly/fashionably/ well/in black ______
fit ______
get changed ______
get dressed/undressed ______

look ______
look like sb ______
match ______
suit ______
try on ______
wear ______

Challenges

achieve ______
be the inspiration behind sth ______

challenging ______
copy ______
fulfil your ambitions ______
give (sth) up ______
inspire ______
keep up with ______
make a list of pluses and minuses ______

make up ______

make sth easier/harder ______________

____

make up your mind ______________

manage to do sth ______________

miss the chance ______________

set out on sth ______________

stressful ______________

take risks ______________

triumph ______________

visualise ______________

Expressing opinions

approve of sth ______________

be in favour of/opposed to sth ______________

____

claim ______________

clarify ______________

come up with ______________

confirm ______________

consider ______________

disapprove of ______________

explain ______________

express your support for/disapproval of sth ______________

insist on (doing sth) ______________

make a point ______________

make an excuse ______________

on the tip of my tongue ______________

____

point out ______________

point of view ______________

refuse ______________

reply/respond ______________

suggest ______________

Home

Location

capital city ______________

current address ______________

halfway down a street ______________

home town ______________

industrial area ______________

in the countryside ______________

local community ______________

neighbour ______________

neighbourhood ______________

megacity ______________

suburbs ______________

Types of houses

detached house ______________

flat ______________

modern ______________

semi-detached house ______________

terraced house ______________

At home

bill ______________

burglar alarm ______________

cut the grass ______________

do the gardening/cooking ______________

____

electricity ______________

front door ______________

gate ______________

lawn mower ______________

lock ______________

make your bed ______________

tidy your bedroom ______________

redecorate ______________

running water ______________

wall ______________

School

after-school club ______________

attend lessons ______________

basic skills ______________

canteen ______________

college ______________

copy sb's homework ______________

do a course (in) ______________

do a degree (in) ______________

do a test ______________

do some revision ______________

do your homework ______________

drop a subject ______________

exclude sb from school ______________

get a place at university ______________

get better marks ______________

gym ______________

head teacher ______________

learn new skills ______________

pass your exams ______________

school grounds ______________

school uniform ______________

single-sex school ______________

skip a lesson ______________

spelling ______________

subject ______________

textbook ______________

tutor ______________

Work

Jobs

artist ______________

builder ______________

bus driver ______________

carpenter ______________

chef ______________

cook ______________

curator ______________

decorator ______________

dentist ______________

director ______________

doctor ______________

editor ______________

electrician ______________

entertainer ______________

farmer ______________

fashion designer ______________

forecaster ______________

jeweller ______________

judge ______________

model ______________

musician ______________

nurse ______
nutritionist ______
pilot ______
policeman/policewoman/police officer ______
politician ______
prison guard ______
producer ______
psychologist ______
ranger ______
reporter ______
scientist ______
surgeon ______
tour guide ______
tour leader ______
travel agent ______
waiter/waitress ______

Employment

contract ______
employ ______
employee ______
(full-time/part-time) job/employment ______
long hours ______
overtime ______
salary ______

Business and industry

business skills ______
company ______
cooperative ______
entrepreneur ______
food industry ______
headquarters ______
make a living from sth ______
make money through sth ______
start your own business ______
successful ______

Family and social life

Family members

ancestor ______
ex (n) ______
ex-husband/ex-wife ______
father-in-law/mother-in-law ______
great-grandfather/great-grandmother ______
great-great-grandfather/great-great-grandmother ______
great-great-grandson/great-great-granddaughter ______
half-brother/half-sister ______
nephew ______
niece ______
only child ______
relative ______
second husband/wife ______
sibling ______
son-in-law/daughter-in-law ______
stepbrother/stepsister ______
stepfather/stepmother ______
stepson/stepdaughter ______
uncle/aunt ______

Love and marriage

break sb's heart ______
couple ______
date (v, n) ______
end a relationship ______
engagement ______
engagement ring ______
fall in love ______
fiancé/fiancée ______
get married ______
go out with sb ______
kiss ______
opposite sex ______
split up with sb ______
stop seeing each other ______
wedding ______

Human relations

agree to do sth ______
appreciate ______
be there for sb ______
be reunited with one's family ______
blow a kiss ______
call on sb ______
close friend ______
encourage sb to do sth ______
fall out with sb ______
force sb to do sth ______
friendship ______
get on well with sb ______
give sb a hand ______
have a good relationship with sb ______
have a lot in common with sb ______
have an argument ______
have similar interests ______
help sb out ______
live up to/match sb's expectations ______
look after sb ______
look up to sb ______
lose touch with sb ______
make a fool of sb ______
make sb do sth ______
make sb's day ______
online friend ______
pull sb's leg ______
put a smile on sb's face ______
put up with sb/sth ______
put your arms round sb ______
show respect ______
show your appreciation ______
socialise with ______
warm sb's heart ______

Free time

become interested in sth ______
be into sth ______

cookery course/lessons ______
get into sth ______
go clubbing ______
hang around in the streets ______
hang out with sb ______
join a club/become a member of a club ______
learn the piano ______
relax ______
sing in a band ______
take sth up ______
youth centre ______

Food

Meat, fish and seafood

bacon ______
beef ______
chicken ______
cod ______
ham ______
lamb ______
prawns ______
red meat ______
salmon ______
sardines ______
sausage ______
shellfish ______
tuna ______

Fruit

apple ______
avocado ______
banana ______
grapefruit ______
grape ______
kiwi ______
mango ______
melon ______
orange ______

Vegetables

beetroot ______
broccoli ______
Brussels sprouts ______
cabbage ______
carrot ______
cauliflower ______
celery ______
chilli ______
corn ______
garlic ______
green beans ______
lettuce ______
olive ______
onion ______
potato ______
red pepper ______
soya ______
spinach ______
tomato ______

Dairy products

butter ______
cheese ______
cream ______
egg ______
milk ______

Drinks

coffee ______
coke ______
fizzy drink ______
juice ______
tea ______
water ______

Dishes

barbequed steak ______
cheeseburger ______
chips ______
fast food ______
fried eggs ______
(green) salad ______
(Indian) curry ______
meat pie ______
omelette ______
pancake ______
pasta sauce ______
pizza ______
pudding ______
risotto ______
sandwich ______
scrambled eggs ______
steak ______
stew ______
sushi ______
(vegetable) soup ______

Sweets and desserts

apple pie ______
biscuit ______
cake ______
chocolate mousse ______
(dark) chocolate ______
fruit salad ______
ice cream ______

Other

(brown) sugar ______
cereal ______
crisps ______
crust ______
jam ______
leftovers ______
mushroom ______
olive oil ______
popcorn ______
rice ______
salt ______
(white) bread ______

Meals

breakfast ______
dinner ______
lunch ______
main course ______
snack ______
starter ______
supper ______

Adjectives describing food

bitter ______
boiled ______
cold ______
cooked ______
crispy ______
delicious/yummy ______
disgusting ______
dried ______
edible ______
fattening ______
firm ______
fresh ______
fried ______
frozen ______
greasy ______
healthy ______
hot/spicy ______
juicy ______
mild ______
raw ______
ripe ______
roast ______
rotten ______
salty ______
smelly ______
sour ______
strong ______
sweet ______
tasty ______
stale ______
tinned ______
ugly ______
unripe ______
warm ______

Cooking

add ______
boil ______
chop (up) ______
cook ______
cup ______
cut up ______
eat up ______
feed ______
flavour ______
freeze ______
fry ______
heat ______
ingredient ______
jar ______
loaf ______
mash (up) ______
mix ______
mixture ______
oven ______
packet ______
pan/saucepan ______
peel ______
plate ______
portion ______
pour ______
press ______
recipe ______
roast ______
serve ______
slice (v, n) ______
smell ______
spoon ______
taste (v, n) ______
texture ______
tin ______

Food and health

animal products ______
balanced diet ______
be allergic to sth ______
eating habits ______
energy boost ______
fresh produce ______
grease ______
heavy/light meal ______
(healthy) lifestyle ______
lose weight ______
nutritionist ______
protein ______
vegan ______
vegetarian ______
vitamin ______

In a restaurant

bill ______
chef ______
cook ______
cuisine ______
menu ______
order (v, n) ______
waiter/waitress ______

Shopping and services

advertiser ______
advertising ______
bank account ______
changing room ______
consumer ______
reduce ______
reduction ______
shop online ______
shopping bag ______
shopping mall ______
size ______
queue/stand in a queue ______
try (sth) on ______

Travelling and tourism

Means of transport

canoe ______
car ______
(cargo) ship ______
double-decker (bus) ______
(express) train ______
ferry ______
(fishing) boat ______

helicopter ____
jeep ____
plane ____

Air/Road/Sea travel

airport ____
arrive ____
baggage reclaim ____
board a ship/a plane/a ferry ____
boarding pass ____
book a ticket/a flight/a hotel room ____
car journey ____
catch a train/a bus/a plane ____
check-in desk ____
collect your luggage ____
cross a sea/a river ____
cross Europe ____
go away ____
departure lounge ____
destination ____
fasten your seat belt ____
fly ____
gate ____
get off ____
go abroad ____
go through passport control/security ____
GPS ____
land ____
map ____
miss a train/a bus/a flight ____
overhead locker ____
passenger ____
pilot ____
reach your destination ____
reservation ____
return journey ____
route ____
sail ____
security check ____
set off (on a journey) ____
stop over ____
take off ____
terminal ____
ticket ____
traffic jam ____
travel agent ____
travel by train/bus ____
travel company ____
travel insurance ____
traveller ____

Types of trips

beach/seaside holiday ____
bus trip ____
business trip ____
city break ____
cruise ____
go backpacking ____
holiday camp ____
overland tour ____
safari ____
school holiday ____
school trip ____
skiing holiday ____
trekking ____

Accommodation

camp ____
campsite ____
(three-star) hotel ____
put up a tent ____
seaside/beach resort ____
single room ____
ski resort ____
stay in/at ____
stay over ____
youth hostel ____

On holiday

embassy ____
get on (your bike) ____
guide book ____
hike ____
holidaymaker ____
location ____
main square ____
move on to ____
outdoor activities ____
overcrowded ____
ride (a horse) ____
row ____
see the sights ____
tour guide ____
tour leader ____
tourism ____
travel arrangements ____
tropical island ____

Adventure and danger

base camp ____
cliff ____
climb ____
climber ____
come down the mountain ____
crash ____
crash into sth ____
disaster ____
emergency call ____
explore ____
knock ____
penknife ____
rescue team ____
risk ____
rope ____
safety ____
survive ____
survivor ____
trap ____
unexpected event ____

Culture

Art

art critic ____
curator ____
gallery ____

painting ______

sculpture ______

work of art ______

Literature

author ______

autobiographical ______

cover ______

describe ______

detective novel ______

extract ______

main character ______

narrator ______

novel ______

poem ______

tell a story ______

Types of TV and TV programmes

cable television ______

chat show ______

documentary ______

music programme ______

quiz/game show ______

reality TV/reality show ______

satellite television ______

sitcom ______

soap opera ______

sports programme ______

talent/music competition ______

the news/current affairs ______

TV channel ______

TV network ______

TV series/serial ______

Television, film, music

action film ______

adaptation ______

advert ______

audience ______

audition (v, n) ______

band ______

be nominated for an Oscar ______

broadcast ______

celebrity ______

challenge ______

chance of winning ______

coach ______

compete ______

competition ______

competitor ______

contest ______

contestant ______

direct ______

director ______

edit ______

edition ______

editor ______

eliminate ______

enter a competition ______

entertain ______

entertainer ______

entertainment ______

episode ______

fail ______

female/male artist ______

festival-goer ______

hidden camera ______

in the spotlight ______

interview sb ______

judge (v, n) ______

live ______

movie ______

movie business ______

music label ______

Oscar ceremony ______

panel ______

perform ______

performance ______

performer ______

photo session ______

play a role ______

pop singer ______

present ______

presentation ______

presenter ______

produce ______

producer ______

production ______

professional ______

recording contract ______

rehearsal ______

reunion show ______

royalty ______

scene ______

screenplay ______

script ______

solo artist ______

song lyrics ______

stunt ______

television personality ______

video clip ______

viewer ______

vote off ______

vote online/by telephone/by text ______

win the title/prize ______

winner ______

Sport

Types of sport

aerobics ______

archery ______

athletics ______

badminton ______

baseball ______

basketball ______

boxing ______

canoeing ______

competitive sport ______

cricket ______

cycling ______

extreme sport ______

football ______

golf ______

hockey ______

ice hockey
individual/team sport
indoor/outdoor sport
jogging
judo
karate
long jump
martial arts
motor racing
rugby
sailing
skating
skiing
snowboarding
squash
summer/winter sport
swimming
(table) tennis
volleyball
wind-surfing
wrestling

Places where you do sport

athletics track
basketball/volleyball court
boxing/wrestling ring
cricket/football/rugby/hockey pitch
cycle/motor racing track
golf course
gym
ice rink
(Olympic) swimming pool
sailing club
ski resort
(ski) slope
squash/tennis court
stadium

Sports equipment

badminton/squash/tennis racket
baseball/cricket bat
boots
golf club
helmet
hockey stick
kit
red/yellow card
snowboard
surfboard
table tennis bat
trainers

People in sport

athlete
captain
coach/trainer
fan
footballer
goalkeeper
opponent
opposing team
player
referee
rival
runner
spectator
surfer
team-mate

Types of sports competitions

cycle race
FA Cup
final
league
(long-distance) race
marathon
match
Paralympics/Paralympic Games
sporting/sports event
tournament
walking race
yacht race

Competing in sports

beat an opponent/the champion
blow a whistle
bounce/catch/hit/kick/pass/throw a ball
break a world record
chase after sb
come first/second/last
compete
dive for the ball
do sport
enter a competition
gold/silver/bronze medal
keep/stay fit, keep/stay in shape
lead
lose a match/a game
lose a point
overtake
position
qualify for
score
score a goal/a point
set a new (world) record
speed
speed up
take part in
training session
win a point
win a prize/a match/a game

Health

Parts of the body

ankle
arm
back
bone
bottom
calf
cheek

chest ______
elbow ______
eyebrows ______
finger ______
fingernail ______
foot ______
forehead ______
heel ______
jaw ______
knee ______
lips ______
neck ______
rib ______
shoulder ______
stomach ______
thigh ______
thumb ______
toe ______
tongue ______
tooth ______
waist ______
wrist ______

Injuries and disabilities

black eye ______
bleed ______
break ______
break your leg/your arm/a rib ______
break your neck ______
broken leg/bone ______
bruise (v, n) ______
bruised elbow ______
burn (n) ______
burn your tongue/finger ______
burnt finger ______
cut (n) ______
cut finger/hand/lip ______
cut your finger/ hand/lip ______
disabled ______
dislocate your shoulder/thumb ______
dislocated shoulder/thumb ______
dislocation ______
fall over/have a fall ______
get a few cuts/bruises/scratches ______
get injured ______
hurt yourself ______
overcome your disability ______
prosthetic leg ______
scratch your knees/neck ______
scratches on your legs ______
(spinal) injury ______
sprain (n) ______
sprain/twist your ankle/wrist/knee ______
sprained ankle ______
sting (v, n) ______
swollen ______
the blind ______
the deaf ______
tragedy ______
unconscious ______
wheelchair ______

Illnesses and symptoms

ache ______
asthma ______
be sick (with) ______
catch (a disease) ______
cold ______
condition ______
contagious ______
cough ______
deadly ______
develop/get symptoms ______
die ______
fall/get ill (with sth) ______
feel dizzy/sick ______
feel well/weak ______
fever ______
flu ______
get (malaria) ______
get worse ______
have a pain in your back/leg/chest ______
have a temperature ______
have no appetite ______
hay fever ______
headache ______
heart attack ______
hurt ______
(seriously) ill ______
indigestion ______
infection ______
kill ______
lose your voice ______
malaria ______
nosebleed ______
poison ______
put on weight ______
rash ______
runny nose ______
sickness ______
(have a) sore throat ______
stomachache ______
sunburn ______
virus ______
vomit ______
vomiting ______
weight problems ______

Treatment

be on a diet ______
breathe in/out ______
cure (v, n) ______
diagnose ______
diagnosis ______
do a blood test ______
examine ______
eye drops ______
eyesight ______
first aid ______
get better ______
give sb an injection ______

go on a diet ______
have your eyes tested ______
(herbal) medicine ______
hospital ______
inject ______
make a complete recovery ______
make an appointment ______
nurse ______
open wide ______
operation ______
patient ______
prescribe ______
prescription ______
prevent ______
prevention ______
put a plaster on sth ______
put ice on sth ______
recover (from a disease) ______
recovery ______
release sb from hospital ______
save lives ______
see a doctor ______
stop the blood flowing ______
surgeon ______
take (antihistamine) tablets ______
take sb's temperature ______
treat ______

Science and technology

The Internet and modern technology

app (application) ______
blog ______
blog entry ______
blogger ______
blogging ______
bring alive ______
broadband connection ______
charge your phone ______
chat online ______
connected to ______
device ______
download ______
earphones ______
feedback ______
file ______
film ______
follow a vlog ______
gadget ______
go viral ______
hit ______
innovation ______
instant communication ______
interact ______
interactive map ______
Internet connection ______
Internet superstar ______
link ______
log on to (Facebook) ______
password ______
phone charger ______
post (v, n) ______
print a document ______
profile photo ______
publicise ______
satellite technology ______
screen ______
set up a webpage ______
share sth with sb ______
smartphone ______
social networking site ______
subscriber ______
switch on ______
switch off ______
text ______
the battery is flat ______
topic ______
tune a radio ______
turn up the volume ______
type in ______
update (v, n) ______
upload (v, n) ______
video ______
video camera ______
view (v, n) ______
viral ______
viral video ______
virtual ______
visit a website ______
vlog (video blog) ______
vlogger (video blogger) ______
webcam ______
white noise ______
YouTube channel ______

Genetics

ancestor ______
be the image of ______
evolution ______
determine ______
(dominant) gene ______
identical twins ______
inherit sth from sb ______
pass sth on ______
resemble ______
scientist ______
take after sb ______
unique ______

The natural world

Landscape

bay ______
blood-red sunset ______
bush ______ ; the bush ______
calm ______
canyon ______
cascade ______
coast ______
continent ______
country ______
dam ______
dense/thick forest ______
desert ______
flow ______

foothills ___
glacier ___
hillside ___
island ___
lake ___
locate ___
location ___
mountain ___
mountain range ___
ocean ___
overlook ___
overlooking ___
peninsula ___
rainforest ___
river bank ___
sea ___
sky ___
sparkling lights ___
steep hill ___
stunning/amazing/perfect view of/over sth ___
unspoilt ___
valley ___
volcano ___
waterfall ___

Weather and natural disasters

climate ___
crack ___
destroy ___
destruction ___
drought ___
erupt ___
evacuate ___
evacuation ___
explode ___
(extinct/active) volcano ___
extreme weather ___
flood (v, n) ___
flooding ___
forecaster ___
ground ___
hurricane ___
(major) earthquake ___
meteorology ___
predict ___
prediction ___
rain (v, n) ___
snow (v, n) ___
rescuer ___
river burst its banks ___
send out hot rocks ___
shake ___
storm ___
strike ___
(strong) wind ___
tornado ___
tsunami ___
tsunami zone ___
volcanic eruption ___
wave ___
weather centre ___
weather forecast ___

Animals

bear ___
bite ___
buffalo ___
cage ___
cattle ___
cheetah ___
dolphin ___
domestic animal ___
eagle ___
elephant ___
feed ___
female elephant/gorilla ___
giraffe ___
goat ___
herd ___
leopard ___
lion ___
on the loose ___
ostrich ___
penguin ___
pet ___
puma ___
rhinoceros ___
roar (v, n) ___
shark ___
tiger ___
trunk ___
whale ___
wolf ___
zebra ___
zoo ___

Environmental issues

(air) pollution ___
air quality ___
climate change ___
damage the environment ___
deforestation ___
endangered (plants/species/wildlife) ___
environment ___
environmental protection ___
global warming ___
illegal logging ___
low-energy light bulb ___
melt ___
natural resources ___
on a global scale ___
organic ___
produce crops ___
public transport ___
recreate ___
recycle ___
recycling bin ___
renewable energy ___
rubbish ___
save energy/electricity ___
solar panel ___
solar power ___
traffic pollution ___
waste (v, n) ___

State and society

Poverty

barefoot ____
be fortunate/less fortunate ____
beg ____
beggar ____
collection cup ____
homeless ____
jobless ____
poverty ____
shelter ____
sleep rough ____
the poor ____

Charity

benefit ____
charity event ____
collect money ____
collection ____
cycle/cycle race ____
do a good deed ____
donate ____
donation ____
foundation ____
in memory of sb ____
offer sb a reward/a job ____
organise a sale ____
participant ____
raise money for (charity) ____
second-hand clothes ____
sponsor ____
take part in ____
voluntary work ____

State and economy

abolish ____
aristocracy ____
authorities ____
community ____
citizen ____
city council ____
constitution ____
demonstration ____
economic growth ____
elect ____
export ____
get access to ____
government ____
health care ____
immigrant ____
inhabitant ____
leader ____
majority ____
organisation ____
overpopulation ____
politician ____
population ____
press conference ____
production ____
provide ____
public institution ____
raise awareness of sth ____
revolutionary ____
revolution ____
standard of living ____
statistics ____

Crime

arrest ____
break the rules/the law ____
burglar alarm ____
burglary ____
burgle ____
case ____
cell ____
commit murder/a crime ____
criminal damage ____
death penalty ____
dig a tunnel ____
escape (v) ____
escape attempt/attempted escape ____
fake ____
follow ____
imprison ____
investigate ____
judge ____
kill ____
lock (n) ____
lock sb (up) ____
make an example of sb ____
murderer ____
policeman/policewoman/police officer ____
prison guard ____
prisoner ____
punish ____
question ____
release sb from prison ____
robbery ____
security firm ____
security lights ____
sentence (n) ____
sentence sb to (death) ____
steal ____
suspect (v, n) ____
theft ____
uniform ____
violence ____
young offender ____

People

1 Complete the tips with the words in the box.

beard bracelet curly flared jeans freckles leather silver ring ~~sunglasses~~ sweatpants

BE TRENDY THIS SUMMER

IN ...

0 It's summer, so *sunglasses* are a must in sunny weather. Don't leave home without them!
1 A pale complexion is in – stay out of the sun. A few _______ are cool though!
2 _______ hair is in – go for a natural hairstyle for the beach this summer.
3 _______ are definitely in. Wear them with sandals or high-heels in the evening.
4 Stylish, handmade jewellery is in – go for a _______ or a pair of earrings to look original.

OUT ...

5 Don't grow a goatee _______ – they're out and you don't want to look like your uncle this summer.
6 _______ clothes are definitely out – we are not going to kill animals for the sake of fashion!
7 Remember to wear _______ only when doing sports. Mind you they should be close-fitting, not baggy!
8 Heavy gold jewellery is out – if you want to look trendy, wear a delicate _______ .

2 Choose the correct answer, A, B, C or D.

0 She is easily hurt by what other people say. She's __ .
(A sensitive) B honest C polite D insensitive

1 Tom is relaxed – he is __ .
A friendly C outgoing
B easy-going D optimistic

2 Which adjective *cannot* be used to describe a bad student?
A immature C hard-working
B rude D lazy

3 Andy has never been afraid of trying new things or taking risks – he is definitely __ .
A adventurous C nervous
B shy D stupid

4 It's incredible how my grandparents have been so loving and __ towards each other for over fifty years!
A mean C caring
B cruel D dynamic

5 As a successful businesswoman, she is a(n) __ role model for all of us.
A sophisticated C loyal
B inspiring D modest

6 Matt always complains about everything – he is so __ !
A grumpy C arrogant
B childish D cheeky

Home

1 Match the words with their meanings.

0 current address [e]
1 neighbourhood [ ]
2 industrial area [ ]
3 suburbs [ ]
4 local community [ ]

a the area on the edge of a city where most people live
b an area with factories rather than houses and flats
c an area of a town/city
d the people living in one area
e the place where you live at the moment

2 Complete the texts with the words in the boxes.

~~countryside~~ detached flat front door home town modern neighbours redecorate

They didn't go to Hawaii or the Caribbean on honeymoon. In fact, they didn't go anywhere as they had spent all their money on buying their first house.

When the wedding reception was over, they immediately got into their old Mini and dashed to the [0] *countryside*, leaving behind the noise of their [1] _______ . Although the house didn't look attractive at first sight, they couldn't wait to see it. Finally, they arrived at a [2] _______ building with a grey façade. It was a [3] _______ house, as Mary didn't like the idea of having noisy [4] _______ on the other side of the wall. They were both excited because they had never lived in a house before – only a [5] _______ – and couldn't wait to [6] _______ their new home. There was only one problem: they had forgotten the key to the [7] _______ !

bill burglar cut gardening gate make mower running tidy wall

We need to set some house rules. The garden [8] _______ must always be closed – the Smiths have a horrible dog. Good thing our [9] _______ is so tall! You will have to turn on the [10] _______ alarm when you go out, but it's easy to use. We [11] _______ our beds in the morning and [12] _______ the bedrooms every other day. I'll pay the [13] _______ for electricity if you pay the one for heating. Of course, we've got [14] _______ water in the bathroom and kitchen – we don't have to get it from the river! By the way, I can do the cooking if you do the [15] _______ – I'm allergic and can't [16] _______ the grass. Yes, we do have a lawn [17] _______ you can use.

School

1 Choose the correct answer, A, B, C or D.

0 She was excluded __ school for her behaviour.
A of
B out
C from (circled)
D on

1 An after-school club is something __ .
A all school pupils attend
B all teachers attend
C some school pupils attend
D parents attend

2 Before an exam, you usually __ .
A do some revision
B do a degree
B copy somebody's homework
D drop a subject

3 You usually eat lunch in the school's __ .
A canteen
B gym
C classrooms
D grounds

4 A tutor is __ .
A a friend from school
B a school teacher
C the head teacher
D a person who gives private lessons

5 A single-sex school is a school __ .
A only for boys
B only for girls
C either for boys or girls
D for both boys and girls

2 Complete the text with the words in the box.

college | do a course | ~~get a place~~ | get better marks | learn new skills | pass your exams | skip lessons

Do you want to [0] get a place at university or [1] ____________ in the future? If you do, you need to remember that you have to [2] ____________ first. If you want to do that, don't [3] ____________ – regular class attendance will help you [4] ____________ in your exams. Once you get a place at university and [5] ____________ there, you will [6] ____________ , which will help you get a dream job later.

Work

1 Complete the names of the jobs in the text. The first letter of each word is given.

MY CLASS

They all used to be in the same class and I used to be their class master. However, each of them had totally different ambitions. For example, Fiona always liked dressing up and made her own clothes. No wonder she became a [0] **f**ashion **d**esigner. Sophie was called the most beautiful girl in school and, since she became a [1] **m**_____ , you can now see her face on the covers of magazines. Tom was very good at Geography and always wanted to travel – now he's a [2] **t**_____ **l**_____ in Africa! Liz, on the other hand, preferred Biology and was good at lab experiments. She is now a well-known [3] **s**_____ . Then there's Pete, who would often read crime stories under his desk. Now I hear he's the best [4] **p**_____ **o**_____ in the whole town! His best school friend, Tim, works as a [5] **j**_____ , and I hear they often meet in court. David, who claimed he was not interested in current affairs, studied Politics at university and is now a [6] **p**_____ . As for Lucy, I always knew she would make a wonderful [7] **d**_____ . I wonder how many hospital patients she has treated successfully. Brenda, another of my students, works in the same hospital as a [8] **n**_____ . She always liked caring for others.

The jobs of my former pupils vary so much. There is a [9] **c**_____ who works in a well-known London restaurant and a [10] **r**_____ who appears on the TV news. You may wonder how I know all this. Well, of course, from Tina, the [11] **d** _____ who takes care of my teeth!

2 Match the words with their meanings.

0 headquarters [f]
1 full-time job [ ]
2 part-time job [ ]
3 salary [ ]
4 contract [ ]
5 employee [ ]

a a job for eight hours a day and five times a week
b money you get from your company once a month for doing a job
c a job, for example, for four hours a day
d a document you sign before you start a job
e a person who works in a company
f the main building used by a company

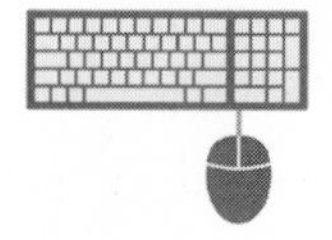

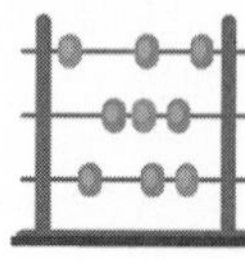

Family and social life

1 Choose the correct answer, A, B, C or D.

0 He was reunited __ his family.
A on B in C at (D with)

1 We have a lot __ common.
A with B in C on D –

2 If you get into something, you __ .
A are interested in it
B aren't interested in it
C hate it
D have to do it

3 Your nephew is __ .
A your sister's son-in-law
B your sister's son
C your sister's husband
D your sister's daughter

4 When you split up with somebody, you __ .
A fall in love
B go out with him/her
C end a relationship
D date him/her

5 The news about his wedding really __ my day.
A made B did C took D had

6 They used to be close friends, but they lost __ after college.
A communication
B friendship
C touch
D interests

2 Complete the sentences with the correct form of the phrasal verbs in the box.

call on	fall out	~~live up~~	look after
look up	put up	take up	

0 The new *Hobbit* movie didn't live up to my expectations – I was disappointed.
1 You look depressed! Did you __________ with your parents again?
2 When John's parents are away for business, he __________ his grandma, does the shopping for her and walks her dog.
3 She'd like to live on her own; she can't __________ with her parents.
4 Mary really __________ to her older sister – she wants to be just like her.
5 Why don't you __________ Ann this afternoon and see if she needs any help with the decorations?
6 After the divorce he __________ diving and sailing. His ex-wife hated water sports.

Food

1 Complete the words in the advertisements. Some letters are given.

If you want to stay fit, drink our juices! Try the [0]**g**rapefruit juice, a great source of vitamin C.

Forgotten your school [1]**l**________ ? Don't worry! Buy our freshly made [2]**s**________**s**. We have dozens of them on offer: cheese, ham, egg – you name it, we have it! They are [3]**d**________ too!

Brighten up your dinner with our [4]**t**________ food. All you have to do at home is open the packaging and [5]**h**________ it up! On our menu we have [6]**v**________ soup, Indian [7]**c**________ and also pasta [8]**s**________ !

2 Choose the correct answer, A, B, C or D.

0 I always eat __ vegetables – I never cook them.
A unripe C crispy
(B raw) D cold

1 First, __ the potatoes and then __ them.
A mash up, peel C roast, cook
B peel, slice D cook, press

2 If you don't cover the bread, it will go __ .
A stale C ripe
B rotten D smelly

3 White __ with butter and honey is good for breakfast, but don't eat too much of it.
A shellfish C bread
B lettuce D mango

4 Before our main course we all had a __ .
A breakfast C supper
B snack D starter

5 She opened a __ of crisps and ate them all.
A jar C packet
B pan D tin

6 Mild food doesn't have any __ spices in it.
A hot C salty
B sweet D sour

7 Which of these is usually made of fish?
A sushi C bacon
B ham D sausage

8 For most people, the __ of food is more important than its appearance.
A mixture C flavour
B vitamin D balanced diet

Shopping and services

1 Complete the words in the text. Some letters are given.

I hate going shopping. Why? Well, first of all, I hate standing in a [0]**q**_ueue_ – it takes so long! Then I always have problems finding my [1]**s**__________ – everything is too small or too big. Usually the right one is in a colour I hate. If I find something (which is not easy, as you can see!), then I need to go to the [2]**c**__________ room to [3]**t**__________ it on, and it's always so hot in there. The mirrors make you look fat! If I finally buy something, they always [4]**r**__________ the price just a few days later and, of course, I can't return the clothes because I've already worn them.

Shopping for food is also bad. I always leave my shopping [5]**b**__________ at home and have to buy one in the store. I can never find anything quickly because they keep changing the location of the products – bread is where the drinks were last month and so on. Oh, and I also get lost in those huge shopping [6]**m**__________**s**.

That's why I shop [7]**o**__________ whenever I can – it's easy, fast and I don't have to leave home! The stores also have great special offers and seasonal price [8]**r**__________. It's even easier now I've opened a bank [9]**a**__________ in an Internet bank. [10]**C**__________ of Internet shops definitely need to have a credit card! Another thing is, there isn't so much [11]**a**__________ online – or if there is, you can easily block it, and you can't do that with posters or TV ads (which is why [12]**a**__________ prefer to use these media – more people see them, whether they want to or not!).

ONLINE SHOP

Traveling and tourism

1 Complete the sentences with the words in the box. Then put the sentences in the correct order.

~~booked~~	boarded	control	gate	locker
luggage	pass	seat belt	security	took

a I _booked_ the flight. [1]
b I looked for my __________ . [ ]
c I fastened my __________ . [ ]
d The plane __________ off. [ ]
e I __________ the plane. [ ]
f I checked in my __________ . [ ]
g I put my luggage in the overhead __________ . [ ]
h I went through the __________ check and passport __________ . [ ]
i I received my boarding __________ . [ ]

2 Are the statements true (T) or false (F)?

0 If you want to go trekking, you go on a cruise. [F]
1 Before boarding, you wait in the departure lounge. [ ]
2 You check in on the plane. [ ]
3 You need a single room if you travel alone. [ ]
4 A resort is a place at the airport. [ ]
5 Double-deckers are usually seen in cities. [ ]
6 You take a ferry on an overland tour. [ ]
7 You move very fast in a traffic jam. [ ]
8 A holiday camp is usually for children or teenagers. [ ]
9 If you stay at a campsite, you often sleep in a tent. [ ]
10 When you want to cross the sea, it's best to use a canoe. [ ]
11 GPS is a technology that helps you find your destination when you're travelling, e.g. by car. [ ]
12 Youth hostels are only for families with small children. [ ]

Culture

1 Choose the correct answer, A, B, C or D.

0 I love watching __ shows. You can learn a lot. And some of those contestants know everything!
(A quiz) C reality
B chat D soap

1 He found his live __ in front of the judges so stressful that he forgot the lyrics to the song.
A game C drama
B audition D audience

2 The band has a(n) __ very early in the morning, to practise new pieces.
A performance C rehearsal
B audition D cover

3 A(n) __ does *not* work in the film industry.
A director C producer
B editor D curator

4 Who wrote the __ for this film?
A image C royalty
B work of art D screenplay

5 This actor played the main __ in my favourite comedy.
A group C script
B character D scene

6 She sang so fast I couldn't understand the song __ at all.
A lyrics C story
B episode D poem

2 Complete the sentences with the correct form of the words in capitals.

0 Film *production* started only yesterday and already there are problems. **PRODUCE**
1 Their __________ at the Royal Theatre was spectacular. **PERFORM**
2 The __________ took place in London. The winner got a job on TV. **COMPETE**
3 She's an excellent __________. I watch all her shows, even the ones about politics! **PRESENT**
4 He works as an __________ – you know, singing, dancing and telling jokes on stage. **ENTERTAIN**
5 Everything that goes on in the house is filmed by __________ cameras, but it's not really a secret – all the people know about it. **HIDE**
6 Tim and his friends are so excited – they're going to New York to sign a __________ contract for their band! **RECORD**
7 The film is an _____ of a Jane Austen novel. **ADAPT**
8 There are too many talented __________. I don't know who to vote for. **CONTEST**
9 Here is a copy of the latest __________ of our magazine. **EDIT**
10 The __________ is a young girl growing up in Italy in the 1950s. **NARRATE**

Sport

1 Complete the text with the words in the box.

extreme golf helmet martial arts motor racing trainer windsurfing ~~wrestling~~

My grandson is keen on sports and that's OK. What worries me though is that whenever he talks about the sports, I feel as if he's speaking to me in a foreign language. For example, he says he prefers [0]*wrestling* to judo because it's more exciting. Every second weekend he goes out with his friends to watch special [1]__________ tournaments. Now he's packing for a sports camp where he's going to try [2]__________. Of course, I mustn't tell his parents about that! He's trying on his new [3]__________ for biking. He says it will protect his head whatever happens! You know what? This very moment he's surfing on my carefully polished shiny floor in the corridor. But my flat is not an ocean and he is not [4]__________! Well, I'm proud of my grandson, but I wish he would take up [5]__________ and play it on my nicely trimmed lawn. It would be a lot safer than all these [6]__________ sports. Anyway, I must finish now. I'd tell you more about my grandson, but my [7]__________ is giving me another archery lesson today, so I must be going! Take care, everybody!

2 Choose the correct answer, A, B, C or D.

0 Which of these is *not* a winter sport?
A skiing (C windsurfing)
B snowboarding D skating

1 You play table tennis with a __ .
A bat C racket
B club D stick

2 He skied down the __ .
A course C ice rink
B court D slope

3 Which of these is *not* a martial art?
A judo C rugby
B karate D kung-fu

4 Which of these is *not* a team sport?
A cricket C volleyball
B baseball D the long jump

5 Which sport is *not* played indoors?
A badminton C basketball
B canoeing D hockey

6 All the __ shouted happily when he scored the last goal.
A opponents C fans
B goalkeepers D coaches

Health

1 Read the definitions and complete the words. Some letters are given.

0 It's when you have a pain in your stomach.
stomachache

1 You probably have it if you sneeze or cough when certain plants blossom. **h**__ __ **f**__ __ __**r**

2 It's a disease that affects a particular part of your body and is caused by a virus or bacteria. **i**__ __ __ __ __ __ __ __**n**

3 If you're allergic to something you eat, you may get this on your skin. **r**__ __ __

4 It's a tropical disease transmitted by mosquitoes.
m__ __ __ __ __ __ __

5 You stick it on your skin when you have a small wound.
p__ __ __ __ __ __ __

6 It's like a finger, but on your foot. **t**__ __

7 You wear your watch on it. **w**__ __ __ __ __

8 You get this if you spend too much time in the sun.
s__ __ __ __ __ __ __

2 Complete the text with the words in the box.

asthma	coughing	fall	feel sick
injured	lose	nosebleed	pain
~~sore~~	stomachache	symptoms	

Doctor, I'm lucky to be alive. When I watch TV for only four hours, my eyes get [0] sore . Surfing the Internet for ten hours gives me a terrible [1]__________ in my back. When I'm on the phone for only two or three hours, I [2]__________ my voice. What's more, I've started to get [3]__________ of allergy to the crisps I munch on when playing computer games. I keep [4]__________ all the time (could it be the beginning of [5]__________ ?) after eating only three or four packets, and my skin gets itchy. Next, when I eat out in my favourite fast food restaurant, which I only do on Tuesdays and Fridays, I get a terrible [6]__________ . Sometimes I even [7]__________ and can't drink any fizzy drinks. When I have PE lessons, I sweat doing even the simplest exercise and [8]__________ over a lot, especially when we play team sports. Last week I even had a(n) [9]__________ , which was really embarrassing because it caused so much fuss. As I am obviously seriously ill, please exempt me from my PE lessons. I am afraid I will get [10]__________ otherwise.

Science and technology

1 Read the definitions and complete the words. Some letters are given.

0 an online camera
webcam

1 an Internet diary
b__ __ __

2 when you send a short message on your mobile phone
t__ __ __

3 a word you use to, e.g. access your computer
p__ __ __ __ __ __ __ __

4 documents or photos kept on a computer or phone
f__ __ __**s**

5 you do this when you need a paper copy of an electronic document
p__ __ __ __

6 you use them to listen to music, e.g. on a bus
e__ __ __ __ __ __ __ __**s**

7 a program on your mobile phone or computer
a__ __

8 something you use when your phone battery is flat
c__ __ __ __ __ __ __

9 when you send files or music online
u__ __ __ __ __

10 somebody who keeps a video blog
v__ __ __ __ __ __

11 a website where you can connect with your friends or people with similar interests
s__ __ __ __ __ **n**__ __ __ __ __ __ __ __ __ __ **s**__ __ __

2 Complete the words in the sentences. Some letters are given.

0 Mary **r**esembles her mother so much – they have the same eyes, nose and mouth.

1 Anthropologists have found the last common **a**__ __ __ __ __ __ __ __ of chimpanzees and humans, which was humans' closest relative.

2 Some **s**__ __ __ __ __ __ __ __ __**s** believe that it is possible that worms exist deep beneath the surface of other planets.

3 We **i**__ __ __ __ __ __ both our looks and illnesses from our parents and grandparents.

4 Tim and Tom are **i**__ __ __ __ __ __ __ __ __ twins – nobody can tell them apart.

5 The theory of **e**__ __ __ __ __ __ __ __ __ says that all species evolved from a single original form of life.

6 At school, children learn basic information about **g**__ __ __**s** and what they determine.

7 Queen Victoria **p**__ __ __ __ __ __ on the illness to her children.

8 Have you seen Tom's new girlfriend? She's the **i**__ __ __ __ of Jennifer Lawrence!

The natural world

1 Complete the words in the text. Some letters are given.

The long-awaited sequel of the famous 1998 disaster movie stars the brilliant Brian Hurrey and Lilian Dress. Hurrey plays Professor Killian, whose aim is to save humanity. The stunning Lilian Dress helps the professor to save the world. And the world has to face not one disaster, but many. First, the air [0]**q**quality on Earth is so bad that it causes climate [1]**c**__________. Heavy rains cause [2]**f**__________**s**. [3]**F**__________**s** predict other disasters to come: strong winds leading to to [4]**t** __________**s** and [5]**h**__________**s**. People have been [6]**ev**__________ from all major cities. Is this all a result of global [7]**w**__________**g**? Will Professor Killian save the planet before humans [8]**d**__________**e** the environment even more and find a new source of renewable [9]**e**__________**y**? You simply must see for yourselves. We can only add that the most exciting scene takes place on a [10]**g**__________**r** in the Antarctic. Animal lovers won't be disappointed either: the ocean scenes include [11]**w**__________**s** and [12]**d**__________**s**!

2 Complete the sentences with the correct form of the words in capitals.

0 The giant panda is an endangered species. **DANGER**
1 The most deadly __________, which killed three million people, was in 1928 in China. **DRY**
2 Pompeii was destroyed by a __________ eruption. **VOLCANO**
3 If we believed all the natural disaster __________, we'd have moved to another continent ages ago. **PREDICT**
4 It's marvellous to see such __________ nature. **SPOIL**
5 Air __________ in Asian cities is horrible. **POLLUTE**
6 Remember to put all the tins and cans in the __________ bin. **RECYCLE**
7 The village's __________ is what makes it so attractive to tourists. **LOCATE**
8 We stayed in a small hotel __________ the mountains. **OVERLOOK**
9 Basically, __________ means there are fewer and fewer trees. **FOREST**
10 We have to find a way to save the planet's __________ resources. **NATURE**

State and society

1 Read the definitions and complete the words. The first letter of each word is given.

0 the state of not having a job
j o b l e s s
1 people getting together and protesting against something, e.g. in the street
d_ _ _ _ _ _ _ _ _ _ _ _ _
2 too many people living in a particular area
o_ _ _ _ _ _ _ _ _ _ _ _ _ _
3 most people
m_ _ _ _ _ _ _
4 give money to, e.g. a charity
d_ _ _ _ _
5 somebody who takes part in something
p_ _ _ _ _ _ _ _ _ _ _
6 unpaid work, e.g. for a charity
v_ _ _ _ _ _ _ _ _ w_ _ _
7 the set of laws and regulations of a specific country
c_ _ _ _ _ _ _ _ _ _ _
8 somebody who pretends to be somebody else
f_ _ _
9 somebody who asks other people for money or food
b_ _ _ _ _
10 choose a leader (e.g. the president)
e_ _ _ _

2 Choose the correct answer, A, B, C or D.

0 We don't need security __ outside the building – there's a street lamp right in front of the door.
(A lights) C lock
B firm D alarm

1 He committed __ and was sent to prison.
A death C murder
B escape D kill

2 The __ said he was not guilty and had not left home on the night of the crime.
A police officer C suspect
B judge D prison guard

3 In general, I think criminals should be __ .
A punished C burgled
B released D followed

4 You will do a good __ if you help him.
A charity C benefit
B donation D deed

5 Would you like to work for a public __ after school?
A government C institution
B community D authorities

6 Abraham Lincoln __ slavery in the nineteenth century.
A abolished C judged
B punished D broke

3 Complete the texts with the words in the box.

arrest awareness begged burglary burgled care citizens collection council criminal cycle escape event foundation immigrant leader memory offender organising press second-hand statistics ~~stole~~ thief

ORCHARD LOCAL NEWS

The police are looking for a person who [0]*stole* twenty packages of anti-aging cream from The Beauty Shop in Oak Avenue last Friday. The shop's personnel are looking for the [1]________ , who ran away at 15.30. They say it was a medium-height, plump woman, wearing a pink dress and an orange hat.

Sunflower Clinic is holding a(n) [2]________ conference on Saturday. The title is 'Health [3]________ For All'. Entry is free. According to [4]________ , a lot of people have problems accessing medical treatment.

A florist store in Skylark Street has been [5]________ by an unknown man who is still at large. The [6]________ occurred last night. The burglar was seen leaving the shop by a witness, who called the police, but the [7]________ managed to [8]________ , taking all the roses that were in the shop.

The Bloom Fund, a(n) [9]________ caring for the homeless and poor in the area, is organising a(n) [10]________ this weekend. The money collected will be spent on rehousing the poorest in Orchard District. The charity [11]________ will be accompanied by a(n) [12]________ race; everybody is invited.

The Bloom Fund is also [13]________ a sale of [14]________ clothes, so have a look through your wardrobes. Every penny counts! The Bloom Fund was set up in [15]________ of Oscar Bloom, the late mayor of Orchard, who [16]________ on the streets as a young man.

The teenager who attacked two elderly ladies in Rose Street and stole their handbags is already under [17]________ . The young [18]________ claimed that he desperately needed money to buy his grandmother some medicine.

The city [19]________ has a new chairperson. The new [20]________ is a(n) [21]________ from Algeria who hopes to raise [22]________ of the problems faced by non-British [23]________ in our town.

4 Choose the correct answer, A, B or C.

0 We've decided to __ a sale of books and DVDs next weekend.
A donate
B inspire
(C) organise

1 I believe that if I __ a good deed every day, I will be rewarded in the future.
A do
B give
C make

2 In winter the government always runs a campaign to help people who sleep __ in big cities.
A badly B rough C barefoot

3 A beggar is a person who __ .
A is looking for a job
B has nowhere to live
C asks you for money or food

4 A(n) __ person doesn't have shelter.
A deaf B elderly C homeless

5 The owner has offered a big __ for the person who finds his lost dog.
A reward
B benefit
C appreciation

6 If you don't know the local customs, you could easily break __ while on holiday in a foreign country.
A a case B the rules C a crime

7 Nobody has been sentenced __ death in this country since the 1970s.
A on B to C with

8 Car __ is a serious problem in my town. Two cars have been stolen this week.
A theft B robbery C burglary

9 The police have __ the person who may have taken the money, but he refused to give any answers.
A followed
B questioned
C investigated

10 Three criminals tried to __ a tunnel under the prison wall.
A dig B lock C drown

11 Is it true that the UK finally __ the death penalty in 1998?
A tuned
B engaged
C abolished

12 After living there for ten years, Raphael finally became a(n) __ of Canada.
A citizen B neighbour C immigrant

13 In her last article, Angela Stuart made a(n) __ about public institutions in the UK.
A point
B excuse
C example